Recipes from the

Whitaker
Wellness
Institute

Phillips Publishing, Inc.
Potomac, MD 20854

Table of Contents

This is not an ordinary cookbook.

For the last 23 years, over 10,000 people have come to the Whitaker Wellness Institute to undergo testing and treatment for heart disease, diabetes, high blood pressure, and other degenerative diseases. They stay for one week and sample the food, which is their primary therapy.

For many of these people, this program has to work or their diseases will continue to progress. People must leave with the sense that they can successfully implement our diet. They've seen that they are not alone. They've realized that people just like themselves have adopted a low-fat, high-fiber way of living and have turned their lives around.

These are some of the recipes we have and do use at the Whitaker Wellness Institute. They work. Many of our diabetic patients have been able to lower or eliminate their use of insulin by using these recipes. And for our patients seeking an alternative to bypass surgery, these recipes give them a far less dangerous, far more pleasant alternative. For patients wishing to eliminate high blood pressure medications and their side effects, these recipes are often the only thing that they need to wean themselves from their drugs.

These recipes are also the most effective weight loss tool you'll ever come across. Unlike quick weight loss promises, the weight sheds more slowly, about 4-6 pounds a month, but it stays off. Cut the processed, unhealthy fats out of your diet and you'll lose weight—it's that simple.

And if you want to just plain live better, these recipes are for you, too. I recommend whole, fibrous, healthy foods that taste good. Using them in your diet will make a definite difference in your life. You'll feel better. You'll have more energy. That new vitality will probably affect your outlook. There's a lot to look forward to.

As I do with my patients, however, I encourage you to make your own modifications to these recipes. I've never considered a recipe to be written in stone. At the Institute, we've had years of success with these recipes. I hope you will, too.

So laugh, love, and enjoy life!

Julian Whitaker, M.D.

Step One
Eat Smart

Congratulations. You've just opened the door to a whole new way of eating and living. This cookbook tells you everything you need to know to fill your life with wholesome, good-tasting foods that will warm your hearth and renew your health. You'll know what kitchen tools you'll need to create mouth-watering masterpieces. You'll learn about food substitutions—replacing nutritionally bankrupt foods with wholesome, flavorful, low-fat, healthy alternatives. You'll learn how to transform the way you eat and, therefore, the way you live.

As for the recipes, these are the very best. Some of the recipes are rich and sumptuous, some of them are quick and light, but each one has its own delightful flavor that can't be duplicated. They're gourmet, and they're good for you.

They're even easy. Healthy cooking is fast and clean. No more standing over skillets full of popping, burning, bubbling grease. No more choking on clouds of billowing, oily smoke. No more cleaning greasy pots and pans. No more sticky stovetops or spattered walls. Instead, there will be a lot of crisp chopping with sharp knives, and quick steaming of zesty vegetables bright with color and bursting with flavor.

But perhaps the most exciting thing about this cookbook is that if you use it, you'll feel better. More energy, more vitality, less sluggishness, rosier cheeks, brighter eyes, nicer skin, and a better outlook—it's all possible with the delicious foods right here in this cookbook.

Create Balance

To build an ideal diet, you need to optimize your nutrient and fiber intake while reducing excessive sugar and "bad" fats (see Step Four, page 33). It's like sailing. A good sailor can use the wind beautifully to fuel his ship's progress, but if he begins heeling so much that he takes on water, he'll capsize his boat. Use vitamins, minerals, and fibers like the sailor uses the wind, for balance and progress. Don't get bogged down by the sugars and fats.

As you build the ideal diet, at some point you should probably consider cutting back or eliminating meat-source proteins. You can replace the meat-source proteins with fruits, vegetables, grains, and legumes. If you eat enough of these whole, natural foods, they'll give you all of the amino acids your body needs to manufacture protein.

Begin replacing the meats and sweets in your diet with foods from the following five categories:

1. Fresh and Frozen Vegetables
2. Fresh Whole Fruits and Healthy Fruit Desserts
3. Raw Nuts and Seeds
4. Nonfat Poultry and Fish
5. Grains and Beans

Take care to eat enough to give yourself all the energy you need—and your nutritional needs will be met.

1. Fresh and Frozen Vegetables

It's hard to know when to stop praising vegetables because they're such a wonderful resource for so many good things. Since they have carbohydrates, proteins, fiber, starch, small amounts of healthy fats, magnesium, amino acids, calcium, trace minerals, chlorophyll, and great taste, they are perhaps the most important type of food you can eat. Vegetables have the added benefit of being low in natural sugars, so anyone can eat them in unlimited quantities.

The human body is ideally designed to consume a vegetable diet, so it follows that ideal proteins come from vegetables, as well as beans, seeds, and grains. The myth that a vegetarian diet is deficient in protein is erroneous.

Make your rule be: Eat a salad a day. Vegetables in Mustard Vinaigrette (page 85)—with fresh broccoli, carrots, and mushrooms—is an excellent choice. If you want a bit more bite, give the Celery-Spinach Salad, on page 88, a try. *Salads & Salad Dressings*, starting on page 79, has 32 salad recipes in all, each one rich in a variety of vitamins and minerals.

2. Fresh Whole Fruits and Healthy Fruit Desserts

Eat *fresh* fruits two or three times a day. They're rich in enzymes, vitamins, and the fiber your body needs to block natural sugars from entering your bloodstream too quickly. Nature intended freshness. We would all do well to comply.

Fresh fruits not only satisfy the sweet tooth, but provide your body with organic waters, fibers, vitamins, minerals, enzymes, and phytochemicals. These important disease-fighting plant chemicals are powerful antioxidants, which help boost your immune system and protect you from a variety of debilitating diseases, including arthritis, heart disease, and even cancer.

Sweets that have been stripped from their original sources and then combined with dangerous fats, artificial flavors, and colors won't supply you with any benefit. In fact, they actually rob you of beneficial nutrients. Sugary foods just set up a craving for more sugary foods, so wait until you are hungry enough to enjoy a sweet, juicy apple.

If your digestive system is sensitive to roughage, or you have trouble biting or chewing fresh fruit, or if you'd simply like to add more variety to the fruit component of your diet, consider juicing. Juicing extracts the healthy, life-giving nutrients and enzymes from fresh produce and gives them to you in a flavorful, satisfying cocktail. What you won't get with juicing are the unhealthy refined sugars, preservatives, and other chemicals commonly found in canned and bottled juices. If you drink the juice extracted from fresh produce, you'll receive close to 100% of the nutritional value of whole, fresh fruits. However, you won't get the health-enhancing effects of fiber, so don't forgo your fresh fruits entirely.

Another delicious way to get fruits into your life is to create healthy, fruity recipes to enjoy. Turn to page 245 and try the wonderful Applesauce Cake with honey, cinnamon, raisins, and applesauce. Banana Bread (page 247) is always a hit, and the Fresh Fruit Delight (page 238) has everything you need. Guests will beg you for these recipes.

You'll notice several of the recipes that follow call for frozen apple juice concentrate. It lends that necessary touch of sweetness and moisture. But, be sure to use a concentrate *without added sugar*. And don't eliminate fresh fruit from your diet just because you're using apple juice concentrate in your recipes.

Re-educate your taste buds and enjoy fruits throughout your day. Eat them whole, drink their nutritious juices, and bake them into your favorite, tempting, fruit dessert.

3. Raw Nuts and Seeds

Nuts and seeds are a cornucopia of flavors, textures, and nutrients, so use them on salads, for snacks, or even as a topping on frozen nonfat yogurt for a refreshing dessert. Use them as a condiment instead of making them the main part of your meal since they are hard to digest.

Remember to always eat nuts and seeds raw, not roasted. Enjoy these foods, but don't go overboard. Eat them in moderation.

4. Nonfat Poultry and Fish

Totally eliminating all animal protein may be difficult or unnecessary. It's okay to eat poultry or fish once or twice each week as long as the fat and skin have been removed. Just be sure you're getting plenty of vegetables, too.

Since you may be used to eating meat every night, reduce your intake slowly. Have a meatless dinner a couple of times a week until you're used to it. Then make it five or more times a week.

You won't miss meat as much as you think if you make up for it in other ways—grains, beans, legumes, and fresh vegetables. At some point, you'll even notice that meat makes you feel tired and sluggish while vegetables leave you raring to go.

Start slowly and stick with it. You're on the right track.

5. Grains and Beans

Our ancestors built their diets around nutrient-loaded grains and beans. Only in recent times, and only in the most highly developed nations, have beans and grains been replaced by meat as the fundamental backbone of our diet. In their unrefined, unprocessed state, grains and beans are rich sources of fiber, protein, carbohydrates, essential fats, vitamins, and minerals.

We were designed to eat these healthy, fibrous foods, and the benefits are numerous. First, fiber keeps sugar from getting into our bloodstream too fast. Second, it acts as a broom in the colon, keeping it clean and literally mopping up excess fats before they can cause any harm. Fibrous foods are also naturally rich in nutrients, such as the antioxidants and vital minerals. You can eat most fibrous foods raw, too, so you get all the enzymes nature intended.

Make grains and beans the "meat" of your diet, just as your ancestors did. In other words, make them the most calorie-dense, satisfying part of your meal. When you have an itch for something that seems naughty, you'll find that a plate of pasta takes care of the craving. And when you're ready, switch over from white pasta to whole grain pastas because they retain more natural fiber, vitamins, and minerals than do white pastas. Or try a hearty pot of Lentil Stew (page 110) seasoned just right with lots of vegetables. You won't miss red meat at all.

The key to satisfying old tastes is to see that your meals are planned and prepared in advance so that when hunger strikes, your healthy meal is ready and waiting.

The Secret to Cooking with Grains

Grains such as bulgur wheat, rice, barley, buckwheat, millet, and oats are such wonderful foods that as you become more and more accomplished at cooking for health, you'll find yourself using them routinely. High in fiber, vitamin, mineral, and protein content, as well as tasty and easy to store, grains are the inexpensive answer for cooks who choose to maintain their own vitality through vital foods.

If you've never cooked with grains, you'll find that they're remarkably easy. They cook well in crockpots, or you can let them soak overnight to reduce their cooking time on the stove. All grains cook in their own sweet time, but each type is done when it's tender and moist inside. It usually takes 40 minutes to an hour. Before you cook any of them, though, put them in a colander and run water over them for a good wash.

To Boil Grains

Use 1 part grain to 3 parts water. Bring water to a good boil, then add the grain. Stir. When the water is boiling a second time, cover, turn down the heat, and cook until the grain has reached a chewable state that satisfies you, usually 40 minutes to an hour. Pour off any excess water before serving.

To Soak Grains

Let the grain soak for 8-10 hours overnight. Pour the soaking water into a pot and bring it to a boil. Add the grain and bring it to a second boil. Most grains will be fully cooked in about 5 to 15 minutes.

To Thermos-Cook Grains

Boil enough water to fill a large fiberglass thermos. Fill ⅓ of the thermos with grain and fill to the top with the hot water. Screw the lid on tightly, and let the thermos sit overnight. By morning, the grains will be fully cooked.

To Oven Cook Grains

Heat the oven to 350° F. In an oven-proof pot or casserole dish, put 1 part grain to 3 parts water. Cover tightly and put it into the oven. Cook for 45 minutes. Onions, other vegetables, or seasonings can be added for a delicious meal, but will tack about 15 minutes onto your cooking time.

Hints

Grinding grains reduces their cooking time and gives them an interesting texture. Grain flakes don't need as much cooking time as whole grain. Sprouted grains are wonderful in casseroles and breads. Turn to page 112 for a great grain recipe—Mock Meatballs.

Step Two

Make Healthy Substitutions

Once upon a time (and not so long ago), the American diet was defined by what was available. In the land of plenty, we've had access to an extraordinary range of processed foods. Careful shopping involved picking and choosing between all the colorful options. Fats, salts, hidden sugars, and chemicals were not on every shopper's mind.

But as we've become aware of the startling link between nutrition and degenerative disease, we've become more concerned shoppers. We're reading labels, which is a step in the right direction. The ultimate goal, however, is to build a diet around foods that have no labels at all—fresh fruits, vegetables, whole grains, beans, nuts, and seeds—and we're getting there.

Until you reach that ideal point, though, there may be some confusion about what's good and what's not. As you make the transition from unhealthy, processed foods to whole, healthy, natural foods, you'll discover that you don't have to sacrifice taste or eating satisfaction. For example, if you adore a baked potato slathered with sour cream, try using nonfat yogurt instead of the sour cream. Yogurt still has the zesty, creamy sourness, but it's actually good for you. If you want the gourmet touch, sprinkle some chopped chives or fresh parsley on top. It's perfect.

How to Substitute

Start the process of substituting slowly if you want to, but stick with it. In a little while, maybe two or three weeks, you'll get used to the cleaner, lighter tastes of the healthier choices. Once you've gotten used to the baked potato with nonfat yogurt, sour cream is likely to make you feel like a slug.

The list of substitutions, on pages 15-18, along with the recipes in this cookbook, will help you make the transition to healthier foods. Change is a gradual process. Use these recipes as much as you can, but when you feel the need to use one of your old recipes, try making it with a few of these substitutions. Keep at it, and after a while you won't need to refer to the list anymore.

The things on this list are meant to be used as flavor enhancers and condiments, not necessarily as the mainstays of your new way of eating. Experiment until you find the combinations that tease your taste buds.

Soon you'll be delighted to find that you're feeling better, more energetic, lighter on your feet, brighter about the world—simply because you're eating better.

Out with the Bad, In with the Good

When you want:	Replace with:	Guidelines:
butter (for cooking)	Butter Buds®* butter flavored mix	At the grocery store. Mix with water according to package directions. Use whenever butter is appropriate.
butter or margarine (as a spread)	small amount of virgin olive oil or fresh flax oil	It's best to avoid butter as a spread, and please stay away from margarine at all costs. Instead, enjoy the fresh flavor of breads on their own. Or, try dipping bread in a bit of olive or flax oil, like the Italians do.
buttermilk cream	nonfat yogurt and nonfat milk	Mix 1 part yogurt with 3 parts milk.
cheese	nonfat cream cheese	In place of cream cheese. Use as equals in recipes.
	or nonfat cottage cheese	In place of regular cottage cheese.
	or nonfat ricotta cheese	In place of regular ricotta cheese.
	or nonfat or low-fat hard cheeses	In place of regular hard cheeses and bleu cheese.
chocolate	carob powder	Use like semisweet chocolate.
coffee	grain beverage coffee	Follow directions on jar.
corn syrup	unsweetened concentrates of fruit juices—apple, orange, grape	Use as equals. Apple is easiest to mask.
egg	egg whites	Use 2 egg whites instead of 1 whole egg.

When you want:	Replace with:	Guidelines:
egg **(for baking)**	egg whites	Use 2 egg whites instead of 1 whole egg.
	or low-fat egg substitute	Follow package directions.
	or tapioca**	Add 1 T. tapioca per egg for pancakes, cookies, etc.
flour	whole grain flours	Use whole grain flour by itself or with other flours in recipes that need to rise.
flour and oil **(as a thickener)**	cornstarch or arrowroot and cooking liquid	Combine 1-2 T. of cornstarch or arrowroot with small amount of cooking liquid or water and mix into a thin paste. Spoon into the sauce you are preparing and stir until it thickens.
ground beef	precooked lentils, kidney beans, pinto beans, fat-free soy protein, or extra-lean ground turkey without skin. No imitation meat.	Great in Mexican dishes, chili, Italian sauces, with egg whites and grains to make patties, casseroles and stews. You can find soy protein in health food stores.
ice cream	frozen bananas, frozen fruits	Freeze peeled ripe banana and put it in blender; change flavor by adding other fruits.
	or nonfat frozen yogurt	Freeze yogurt with fruits or flavorings, blend for creamy texture.
jelly	lightly sweetened or unsweetened jelly	Use like any jelly.
mayonnaise	Miracle Blend	Recipes for Miracle Blend White and Brown Dressings are on page 230.
	or Mock Mayonnaise	Drain nonfat yogurt with a cheesecloth. In a blender, combine 2 parts drained yogurt to 1 part low-calorie creamy cucumber dressing. Add a pinch of dried dill or your favorite herb. Blend until creamy.

When you want:	Replace with:	Guidelines:
milk	nonfat milk *or* soy or rice milk	Use as equals. Available at most health food stores.
oil (in cooked and baked foods)	Butter Buds*	Available at grocery store. Mix with water according to package directions. Use equal amounts of liquid Butter Buds to oil.
	or lecithin	Use 1 t. in recipes calling for ¼ cup of oil. Add more liquids to recipe to make up for lost moisture.
	or fruits and vegetables	Make up for the oil's moisture in baked goods by adding mashed banana, applesauce, shredded carrot, or zucchini.
oil, butter, or margarine (for pan coating when baking or frying)	nonfat cooking spray such as PAM® or Bertoli's®	Follow directions on spray can label.
peanut butter	Nutty Butter	Blend 1 big ripe banana and, while blender is running, add 2 T. unhulled raw sesame seeds, 6 T. food yeast flakes, (available at most health food stores) ¼ t. vanilla, and ⅛ t. cinnamon. Keep in refrigerator.
	or Raw nut butter	You can get almond, sesame, and other nut butters at many health food stores.
pie crust	Grape-Nuts® cereal	Use plain, original Grape-Nuts. Put into pie tin about ¼- to ½-inch thick. Moisten with fruit juice. Produces graham cracker-like crust when you bake it.
poultry	whole fresh mushrooms	In pasta and noodle dishes, chow mein, casseroles, spaghetti sauces, and with rice.

When you want:	Replace with:	Guidelines:
poultry (cont.)	*or* tofu	Tofu and tempeh are available at health food stores.
salt	Salt Sub	Mix 4 parts onion powder, 2 parts paprika, 2 parts garlic, and 3 parts cayenne pepper.
	or vegetable broth seasoning, without salt	Vegetable broth seasoning is widely available. Look for it in the spice section of your grocery store. A good brand to try is made by Bernard Jensen Products 800-755-4027. Substitute 3 times as much vegetable broth seasoning for the salt in the recipe.
	or powdered sea kelp	Use as equals.
	or none at all	Salt is generally unnecessary; try to avoid it.
sour cream	nonfat sour cream	In place of regular sour cream.
	or skim milk ricotta with nonfat yogurt	Use yogurt to thin ricotta.
	or Mock Sour Cream	Combine 1 can chilled evaporated skim milk with 2 t. lemon juice until mixture thickens. Fold in 3 T. plain nonfat yogurt. Makes 2 cups.
soy sauce	low-sodium soy sauce	Use as directed.
stock	liquid from cooked vegetables or soup	When you cook vegetables, potatoes, etc., save liquid for stock.
	or vegetable broth powder	Add water and make stock.
sugar, brown	date sugar	Use as equals.
sugar, white	honey	Sweetens more, so use less.

When you want:	Replace with:	Guidelines:
sweetener	dried fruits—raisins, dates, prunes, or prune juice, dried apricots, etc. *or* real vanilla, almond, orange, lemon extracts	Use to taste. Use approximately 1 t. per 1 cup of sweetener.
sweetener	Stevia	Stevia is a concentrated natural sweetener made from a South American herb. It's available at many health food stores or can be ordered directly from Body Ecology 800-4-STEVIA. It's very concentrated, so use sparingly.
whipped cream	whipped cream substitute	Blend until frothy: ¾ cup non-fat milk, 1 cup nonfat cottage cheese, uncreamed cottage cheese, hoop cheese, or farmer cheese, and 1 T. real vanilla. *or* Sprinkle ½ cup of ice water with ¼ cup of nonfat milk powder. Beat until thick, add ¼ to ½ t. of vanilla, and a dash of honey.
white bread	whole grain bread	See shopping guide at end of recipe section.
Worcestershire sauce	low sodium soy sauce with apple juice	Mix 1 can thawed apple juice concentrate with 1 bottle low-sodium soy sauce.

* A cholesterol-free butter substitute that comes in packets or shakers. Adding water gives it a buttery texture. Available in most grocery stores and health food stores, or see mail order list at the end of the recipe section on page 251.

** A beady starch and wonderful thickener that comes from the cassava root. It's in the spice section or the baking section at the grocery store.

Step Three
Convert Your Kitchen

The time has come to transform your kitchen into a place where healthy cooking happens naturally. This step can be a lot of fun if you look at it as redecorating instead of overhauling.

Depending on how well your kitchen is already outfitted, you may only need to get rid of a carton of whole milk and a stick of margarine. Otherwise, you may need to make a trip to the local kitchen store or Saturday's yard sale to pick up some wonderful kitchen utensils.

Before you get rid of anything, however, make sure you have some of the right replacements on hand, whether it's a can of pan-spray, such as PAM, some beautiful vegetables, or a good cheese grater. When you've got some of the things you need, begin tossing the things you won't be using anymore. Throw out the processed oils and fatty dairy products altogether, and put your old pans in a pile. Schedule a trip to the Goodwill Industries collection site.

Reward yourself with a stunning dinner from this cookbook. Try fresh lettuce, Honey-Lemon Dressing (page 98), steamed vegetables and Creole Lentils (page 109), followed by Berry Cobbler (page 246). You'll love it.

Regardless of where you are now on your path to optimal health, keep going. Don't stop. Converting your kitchen is one of the most important moves you can make toward living a healthier life. When your kitchen is in shape, you'll find the path of least resistance will be the very best path of all.

Use the Right Equipment

This list tells you what tools you need to have at your fingertips to make your new kitchen as practical as possible. You'll probably have some of these things, and if you don't, you can generally find them at reasonable prices.

Cutting Board

First and foremost, you will need a professional-size cutting board. Those tiny ones you find in most grocery and dime stores won't suffice when you begin preparing the amounts of vegetables and fruits that a good, healthy diet necessitates. Get out the yellow pages and call a restaurant supplier. They almost always have cutting boards big enough to cover a 2-to-3 foot square of your counter top—exactly what you need.

Since you won't be working with much meat, a wooden cutting board will do fine. If you do cut meat on it, wash it extremely well since bacteria can get into the grooves the knife makes.

Vegetable Scrub Brush

Washing vegetables is a must because, unless they're organic, there are probably lots of pesticides in their skin. Run vegetables, like broccoli, under hot water and rinse. Scrub and peel vegetables like non-organic carrots and potatoes (for more details on the thorough washing of non-organic fruits and vegetables, see page 31).

Of course, if organic vegetables are available, by all means buy them, but even they need cleaning. Keeping a scrub brush at the sink is a wonderful idea. Whenever you've got organic potatoes, yams, or carrots, simply scrub them down instead of peeling them. You'll be far more likely to eat them in their fibrous, vitamin-rich skin if you know they're organic and truly clean. The same goes for fruits.

Vegetable Steamer

Since fresh—and freshly cooked—vegetables are the backbone of a vital and healthy diet, steamers are one of the handiest things you can have in the kitchen these days. Your vegetables will be crisp and flavorful. You can buy a stainless steel model at the grocery store for about $5. Get a big one. You'll need it.

Salad Spin-Dryer

Salad spin-dryers are one of the most efficient tools you can get for your kitchen. They save time by eliminating the need to air or towel dry freshly washed lettuce leaves. They protect your salads from sogginess. And on top of all that, you'll find salads taste far more vibrant when they're dressed with tangy taste, not excess water.

Chef's Knives and Sharpener

Reshaping your diet to include more vegetable-based fare calls for a good, dependable set of knives. You'll want a large knife that can be filed razor-sharp for chopping vegetables for soups, salads, and stews. You will also need a serrated knife. You'll find it indispensable for cutting tomatoes, onions, and all the other slippery vegetables and fruits. If you're going to spend the money on a truly good set of knives, spend a little more for a knife holder (wooden or otherwise) to protect the knives from dents, chips, and premature dulling.

It should go without saying that a knife sharpener will be invaluable. You should be able to find professional-quality knives such as those by Henckels, Wusthof-Trident, and Sabatier at a local department store. The best sets range in price from $100 to $200 and usually come with a storage block and sharpening steel. Otherwise, look for a sharpening steel that has a long wand-like device that does the sharpening. It's what the professionals use and what you should use.

Garlic Press

When you begin cooking with less fat, less salt, and more vegetables, you will surely use more fresh garlic. Find a press with a self-cleaning mechanism. The nutcracker-like press that flips back over itself for self-cleaning is the best. Otherwise, the squeezed garlic skin can be difficult to clean out of the tiny holes.

Grater

When you increase your salad consumption, you will enjoy being able to grate carrots, zucchini, and other vegetables into the salad for added flavor and easier eating. A flat stainless steel grater—with a handle—is the easiest to clean because it's the easiest to hold.

Many food processors have a grater blade attachment that works well and is easy to clean. If you've got one, stick with it.

Blender

Because you won't be using bad fats or other heavy sticky ingredients anymore, an inexpensive blender is fine. Buy one for under $30. Just make sure it's got the one feature you need—the ability to blend from very low to very high speeds.

Non-Stick Cookware

To successfully cook without adding oil you'll need non-stick cookware. Avoid aluminum; it makes its way into your food. Calphalon, however, is a dependable brand of aluminum cookware. During manufacturing it goes through a process that seals its pores so the aluminum doesn't react with your food at all.

Probably the best cookware you can buy today is stoneware. This is a *type* of cookware, not a brand. You can find every kind of pan, pot, and baking dish imaginable in stoneware. Most of the better department stores will carry it. Or you can call Colonial Garden Kitchen 800-245-3399.

As far as easy cooking and good health go, investing in an entire cookware set will be well worth the money.

Non-Stick Cookware Utensils

You'll find that using non-stick cookware almost exclusively will increase your need for wooden spoons and spatulas, as well as plastic or nylon spoons and scrapers. Accidentally scraping the non-stick coating with a metal fork ultimately renders the cookware useless because things start sticking.

In addition to that, once the gouges start, they multiply rapidly. While you are probably not at risk if you scrape some of the non-stick coating into your dinner, the cookware loses some of its non-stick capability.

Stainless Steel Cookware

It is not necessary to add these in addition to the non-stick cookware, but if you wish, or if you already have them, extra large pots of stainless steel are handy for soups, sauces, and other liquid cooking. Revere Ware and Cuisinart both make great stainless items with copper bases that conduct heat beautifully.

Corning Ware

Using Corning Ware or any oven-safe cookware with lids is a handy way to cook rice or grains when you don't have time to watch or stir. It's also great for cooking quick "one pot" meals.

Hand Mixer

The minimum you will want is an inexpensive mixer with two beaters for whipping egg whites or whole grain, nonfat batters for cakes, cookies, and pancakes. While a large, expensive mixer is probably more than you'll ever need, hang onto one if you've already got it. A big mixer might come in handy if you cook for company or if you have a very large family.

Large Bowls

When you switch to a high-fiber, low-fat diet, you eat more. While salads used to fit into a thimble they don't anymore. Now you'll likely need 3-, 4-, and 6-quart bowls for your food prepartions. Investing in an unbreakable set of bowls is important.

Some salad eaters prefer Corning Ware bowls; others are happiest with stainless steel. The important thing is that now you need more than just one big bowl for mixing a cookie batter.

Optional Tools for the Best Kitchen Ever

These tools are not essential, but are certainly nice to have handy in your kitchen:

Bread Maker	Non-Stick Waffle Iron
Crockpot	Pasta Maker
Double Boiler or Pressure Cooker	Rice Cooker
Hot-Air Popcorn Popper	Yogurt Maker
Juicer	

Restock Your Shelves with Natural Goodness

Restocking is one of the most logical steps you can take on your path toward a healthier life. If your kitchen is full of fatty dairy products, marbled meats, luncheon loaves, and margarine, that's exactly what you'll end up cooking. If, however, your kitchen has a canister of whole wheat flour, a bottle of vinegar, a safe sweetener like apple juice concentrate, some lentils, and fresh vegetables, that's what you'll use instead.

If you want to invigorate your cooking, invite good health into your kitchen by stocking it with just enough of the right foods. By the way, you don't have to go to the health food store to get these things. The local grocery store probably carries most of them.

Shop Often and Shop Smart

When you do go to the store, don't make the mistake of buying an entire week's worth of fresh foods. Since fresh foods aren't loaded with preservatives, they'll go bad. And don't go out and get every bean, rice, grain, and condiment that looks inviting. Buy smart. Buy the essentials you'll be using time and again, and then, based on the recipes, buy what you need when you need it.

Following is a list of kitchen basics. Once you're firmly rooted in the healthy cooking camp, you'll find you always want to have these handy.

The Essentials

Condiments, Seasonings, and Fat Substitutes

Extra Virgin Olive Oil

Flax Oil

Herbs and Spices (use your favorite; try basil, curry, cinnamon, vanilla, etc.)

Honey

Leaveners (baking soda, baking powder)

Mustard (there are many kinds; choose your favorite)

No-Oil Dressings

Nonfat Cooking Spray (use sparingly in place of oil for pan cooking or baking)

Onions

Grains, Beans, Pasta, and Starches

Arrowroot (for thickening)

Beans—dry black, garbanzo, and pinto

Brown Rice (long grain is dry and fluffy; short grain is moist and chewy)

Cornstarch (for thickening)

Lentils

Pasta

Whole Wheat Flour

Dairy

Egg Whites

Nonfat Milk

To Keep on Hand

Besides the essentials, there are a few other things you'll want to have around. Some of these foods are on the substitution list, *Out with the Bad, In with the Good* (pages 15-18), some of them are just flavor enhancers, and some of them you'll find you can't live without.

For Baking

Butter Buds

Dry Baking Ingredients—baking soda, unsweetened carob powder, tapioca, and active dry yeast

Extracts—lemon, orange, almond, and vanilla

Flavorings—low-sodium soy sauce

baking powder (Rumford® or another brand without aluminum)

Sweeteners—chopped dates, date sugar, frozen apple juice concentrate, fruit preserves, fruit syrup without sugar, unsulphured molasses, raisins, raw honey, Stevia concentrated natural sweetener, 800-4-STEVIA

Vegetable Broth Seasoning, low-salt or no-salt versions. Try Bernard Jensen Products' brand, 800-755-4027. Substitute 3 times as much vegetable broth seasoning for the salt in your recipes.

For General Use

Juices of all types, unsweetened

Mushrooms

Pineapples

Salsa with tomatoes, green chilies, and onions

Spaghetti Sauce (fat-free, low-sodium, meatless)

Tomato Catsup with honey and no salt

Tomato Paste

Tomato Puree

Tomatoes

The Secret to Cooking with Herbs and Spices

There's always going to be someone who complains, "Cutting out fat cuts out all the flavor!"

It's not true in the least. Yes, fats do have a distinctive taste and if that's what you're used to, no doubt you'll notice it when it's gone. But by no means do fats provide all the flavor.

That's where the beauty of herbs and spices comes in—herbs and spices can turn an otherwise ordinary dinner into a sublime experience of mouthwatering subtlety or an explosion of tantalizing flavor. It's up to you.

This brief guide will help you explore the full range of taste sensations.

Herbs and Spices

The Aromatics

ALLSPICE *has a cinnamon-nutmeg-clove flavor*

ANISEED *tastes like licorice*

BASIL *is savory and sweet*

BAY LEAF *is bittersweet*

CARDAMOM *tastes like a ginger cinnamon mixture*

CHERVIL *tastes like licorice*

CINNAMON *has a musky, gentle flavor*

CLOVES *taste woody, dark, and musky*

CORIANDER *tastes like lemon peel and sage*

DILL *has a sweet flavor*

FENNEL *tastes like licorice*

FENUGREEK *has a bitter flavor*

GARLIC *has a pungent oniony taste*

MACE *tastes like nutmeg*

NUTMEG *has a woody rich taste*

PARSLEY *has a woody flavor*

ROSEMARY *has a hint of evergreen*

SAGE *is earthy, musky*

SAVORY *has a mild lemony-mint flavor*

TARRAGON *tastes a bit like licorice*

THYME *is mild and fragrant*

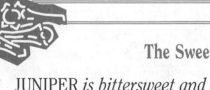

The Sweets and Bittersweets

JUNIPER *is bittersweet and tastes like pine*

MARJORAM *is bittersweet; it makes a great salad herb*

OREGANO *is bittersweet and has a savory lingering taste*

PAPRIKA *can be mild or hot and subtle or sweet*

POPPY SEEDS *have a nut-like texture and very little flavor*

SAFFRON *is sweet, spicy, and mild*

SESAME SEEDS *have a nutty flavor and texture*

VANILLA *has a sweet chocolate-like taste*

CARAWAY *makes foods taste richer*

CAYENNE *tastes like ground red pepper*

CHILI POWDER *is hot and makes your nostrils flare*

CUMIN *adds a yellowish color and pungent taste*

CURRY *is pungent*

GINGER *has a hot sweet flavor*

MINT *is quite aromatic and clean*

MUSTARD *adds a yellow color and is hot and spicy*

PEPPER *is hot; white is milder*

TURMERIC *tastes savory and spicy; adds a yellow color*

Stay Pesticide-Free

Pesticides are a dismal fact of life for those of us who rely on fresh fruits and vegetables. The best way to handle the problem is to buy organic whenever possible—that means produce grown without any sort of pesticide or chemical.

For a long time, we were all told to eat vegetables in their skin, because that's where most of the vitamins and minerals are found. But since 75-80% of the pesticides are on the skin too, you should only eat the skin if you're eating fruits and vegetables that have been organically grown. If you don't have the luxury of shopping at a store that stocks pesticide-free food, ask your local grocery store to consider carrying clean potatoes, grapes, carrots, and apples. Or ask for the address of the nearest co-op.

If you can't buy organic, the best thing you can do is carefully wash and peel store-bought fruits and vegetables. This is especially true for apples, green peppers, cucumbers, and other produce that's routinely waxed. Wax literally cements the pesticides onto the skin of the fruits and vegetables. Try to avoid it.

Skinning a waxy green pepper is a particularly tricky task. Either hold it over a flame to blacken it so the skin will rub off, or parboil it so the skin just falls off. Peel other produce, even melon, in a circular fashion instead of slicing the knife through the skin and into the heart first. This way you avoid transferring the toxins from the skin into the "meat" of the produce.

Do your liver a favor and wash everything. Your liver is the organ in charge of detoxification, and in this day and age, it's overworked because of all the unavoidable toxins we ingest, inhale, or absorb through our skin. The liver is capable of handling the additional burden—to a point. Unfortunately, since we can't know the exact point at which the liver will be overwhelmed, the best thing we can do is to eliminate as many toxins as possible.

If you're in perfect health and want to stay that way, thoroughly wash and scrub fruits and vegetables, like beans or grapes, under hot water.

If your liver is already showing signs of being overwhelmed by today's toxic burden, you should be more vigilant about keeping additional pesticides out of your body. Wash your produce using an all-natural, biodegradable cleanser such as Healthy Harvest, available at most health food and gourmet food stores.

Step Four
Free Yourself from Bad Fats

We are all finally getting the message, loud and clear: Most fats, such as oxidized and non-essential fats, are detrimental to our good health. They clump red blood cells together, harden and clog our arteries, and block the passageways that allow oxygen-rich blood to circulate throughout our bodies. The goal is to eliminate these bad fats altogether. It won't happen overnight, but it certainly can happen slowly. And you'll feel the difference. Once you get used to replacing fatty foods with fibrous healthful choices, a bite of the fatty stuff will probably leave you feeling heavy and dull.

To help you get a handle on bad fats, here are a few fat definitions and facts you should know:

Hydrogenation

Hydrogenation is a process that makes liquid fats more solid and extends their shelf life. Good for the grocer, but bad for you. It involves exposing liquid oil or soft fat to high temperatures, placing it under pressure, and then bubbling hydrogen through the oil. This process changes naturally occurring fatty acids into unnatural fat molecules that are dangerous. They're called trans fatty acids.

Trans Fatty Acids

Trans fatty acids are unstable and don't fit anywhere in your body so they turn into free radicals that roam around your body attacking your cell membranes.

In addition, trans fatty acids clog your arteries and change the way your body burns fat. They raise your harmful (LDL) cholesterol while lowering your good (HDL) cholesterol. They double your risk of heart attack and contribute to cancer, diabetes, and obesity. They also adversely affect reproduction and lactation. To avoid trans fatty acids (hydrogenated fat), read labels and stay away from margarine.

Saturated Fat

While you're reading labels, take notice of saturated versus unsaturated fats. Saturated fats come from animal sources and tropical oils, such as coconut and palm oil. They're considered non-essential fats.

Saturated fats are more difficult for your body to metabolize and have been linked to increased heart risks, cancers, and other diseases. Saturated fat is solid at room temperature, whereas unsaturated fat is fluid. Animal fats are generally higher in saturated fat than vegetable fats. Just visualize the difference between lard and olive oil, and you'll remember which fats to avoid.

Getting Good Fats

Focusing on fat, and keeping it at a healthy level in your diet, is absolutely essential. That doesn't mean banishing fat entirely. Some fat is natural and can actually be good for you. Good fat? Sounds like a misnomer, but it isn't. Let me explain.

Your body needs the right kind of fat to keep its systems lubricated and running smoothly, just like a car engine needs the right kind of oil. Good fats—essential fatty acids (EFAs)—such as Omega-3 and Omega-6, aid in digestion, help your body absorb vitamins, and form the building blocks for many of your body's hormones.

Essential fatty acids are necessary for healthy blood and clean, strong arteries. They help create robust cell membranes, which attract oxygen, transform light into energy, and convert electrical energy to clarify communication along the intricate networks of your nervous system. Good fats energize your digestive, circulatory, and nervous systems.

What makes a good fat good, or a bad fat bad can't be seen or felt. It all has to do with the structure of the fat molecule. Good fats are active and able to make healthy cell membranes and many other things necessary for optimum health. But, the molecular structure of a good fat is destroyed by heat, air, light, and chemical processing, giving rise to free radicals, which can be damaging and potentially deadly.

The problem is, even though your body needs good fats, or essential fatty acids, it can't manufacture them, so you have to look outside your body for help. Where? Flax oil and fish oil are two rich sources of good fatty acids. You'll find both in your health food store or order them from Spectrum Naturals, 800-955-6445 or Healthy Directions, Inc., 800-722-8008, ext. 200. Healthy Directions, Inc. also carries fish oil supplements in convenient gel capsules.

Flax Oil

Flax oil contains the two essential fatty acids from which all others can be made. The first is linoleic acid, or LA (the "parent" of the Omega-6 family of fatty acids); the second is linolenic acid, or LNA (the "parent" of the Omega-3 family of fatty acids). A series of enzyme conversions turns both LA and LNA into forms of fat our bodies can use, called GLA (gamma-linolenic acid) and EPA (eicosapentaenoic acid), respectively. Flax oil has both LA and LNA.

Because of the extreme instability of the fatty acids in flax seeds, they are pressed without any heat, air, or light. They are then immediately packed in dark, opaque bottles, sealed with nitrogen, dated, and refrigerated.

Once home, flax oil should be refrigerated or kept in the freezer. It won't freeze solid and will, if unopened, stay good up to a year. Use it on salads, in blender drinks, on popcorn—anywhere you can. When you do use it, eat it without delay because too much exposure to the air will begin to damage the fragile oil.

Don't cook with flax oil, however. Its health benefits are destroyed by heat. Instead of greasing your cookware with oil, butter, or margarine, use non-stick cookware or, if necessary, use a little pan-spray.

Fish Oil

Fish oil supplements are the best source for pre-formed EPA. You may get some by eating cold water fish, such as salmon, but the bulk of essential fatty acids are either in or directly under the fish skin, which we don't normally eat. Also, some of the oils become damaged when cooked. In addition to fish oil supplements, both evening primrose oil and borage oil provide essential fatty acids in easy-to-use supplement form.

Minimize Cooking With Oil

If you absolutely can't give up the oil in your favorite recipe, please stick with extra virgin olive oil, available at most grocery stores, or crude, expeller oils (except peanut oil) pressed from organically grown seeds. Health food stores carry these. Stay away from all oils known as the "amber oils," such as corn, safflower, sunflower, and other vegetable oils. These are polyunsaturates and have been ruined by processing.

A few of the recipes in this cookbook do include oil as an ingredient. In some of the recipes, the oil is added after cooking. Otherwise, the recipes will call for only a small portion of oil divided among 4 or 5 servings, which results in less than 1 teaspoon of oil per person. Remember, however, oil is optional in each recipe that calls for it. If you'd like, substitute a different ingredient to provide the needed moisture—try water, fruit juice, bananas, shredded carrots, or applesauce.

Read Labels Carefully

Read labels carefully. Don't skim them, *read* them. Reach for foods that have fat contents of 20% or less. Don't be fooled by advertising that calls something "light" or "low-fat." Check the label to make sure they truly are.

Some foods that claim to be fat free are actually far from it, so be careful. Fleischmann's® Extra Light Margarine, for example, is 99% fat. Weight Watchers® Light Salad Dressing is 90% fat. Sizzlean® Bacon is 72% fat, even though the label says it's got 50% less fat. Campbell's Healthy Request® Cream of Mushroom Soup, labeled 99% fat free, is actually 30% fat.

Getting out of the grocery store alive these days is a major victory. But there's hope. Miracle Whip® Free Mayonnaise has 0% fat; same with Seven Seas Free Salad Dressing. Healthy Choice® Chili Beef Soup has 6% fat; Oscar Mayer® Healthy Favorites chicken breast lunch meat has 17% fat; and Kraft® Free Singles Cheese has 0% fat.

Of course, the best solution of all would be to select natural, whole, organic foods. But now that you've got all the facts, begin taking the steps to transform the way you cook and the way you live.

Use these recipes. We love them. You will, too.

Cookbook Keys

Abbreviations

Cup = c.
Gram = gm
Milligram = mg
Ounces = oz.
Pound = lb.
Preparation time = Prep. time
Tablespoon = T.
Teaspoon = t.

Measurements

2 ounces = ⅛ pound
4 ounces = ¼ pound
8 ounces = ½ pound
16 ounces = 1 pound
3 teaspoons = 1 tablespoon
2 tablespoons = 1 fluid ounce
4 tablespoons = ¼ cup or 2 ounces
8 tablespoons = ½ cup or 4 ounces
1 pint = 2 cups or 16 ounces
2 pints = 4 cups or 1 quart or 32 ounces

Conversions

Cereals and Grains

Barley
1 cup = 3 ½ cups cooked

Buckwheat
1 cup = 2 ½ cups cooked

Bulgur Wheat
1 cup = 3 cups cooked

Millet
1 cup raw = 3 ½ cups cooked

Oats
1 pound rolled oats = 5 cups uncooked

1 cup = 1 ¾ cups cooked

Whole Wheat Flour
1 pound = 3 ¾ cups

Vegetables

Asparagus
1 pound spears = 3 ½ cups
  cooked

Beans, green
1 pound = 3 cups cooked

Broccoli
1 pound head = 2 cups cooked
  florets

Cabbage
1 pound = 6 cups shredded =
  2 ½ cups cooked

Carrots
1 pound = 3 cups sliced

Celery
1 ¼-pound bunch = 3 cups diced
  = 2 cups cooked
2 medium ribs = 1 cup sliced

Eggplant
1 pound = 15 1/3-inch slices =
  4 ½ cups diced raw = 1 ¾ cup
  cooked = 3 cups raw

Garlic
1 large head = 12-16 cloves
1 small clove = ½ t. minced = ⅛ t.
  garlic powder

Garlic (cont.)
1 medium clove = ¾ t. minced
1 large clove = 1 t. minced
3 large cloves = 1 T. minced

Mushrooms
1 pound fresh = 5-6 cups sliced

Okra
1 pound fresh = 2 ¼ cups cooked

Onions
1 pound = 3 large = 1 cup diced
  or chopped
1 medium = ⅔ cup chopped
1 small = ⅓ cup chopped

Potatoes
1 pound = 3 medium = 3 ½ cups
  raw sliced = 2 cups cooked

Spinach
1 pound fresh = 4-8 cups raw
  leaves = 2 cups cooked

Zucchini
1 pound = 3 cups raw slices =
  1 ½ cups cooked

Miscellaneous

Big Beans
1 cup uncooked = 2 ½ cups
  cooked
1 pound = 2 cups uncooked or
  5 cups cooked

Lentils
1 cup = 3 cups cooked

Navy Beans
1 pound = 2 ⅓ cups uncooked
  and 5 ½ cups cooked

Pasta
2 ounces spaghetti = 1 cup
  cooked
1 cup small pasta = 1 ¾ cups
  cooked

Rice
1 pound = 2 ½ cups cooked
1 cup raw = 3 cups cooked

Wild Rice
1 cup raw = 4 cups cooked

A small box next to each recipe lists contents you'll want to know as you travel down the path to healthier cooking. This *Per Serving* is a key to the contents in each serving of that particular recipe. Following is a list of the items you'll find in the Per Serving box, and a definition of what each number means. All ingredients listed for each recipe have been included in the per serving calculation—*except* ingredients listed as optional.

Total Fat: This number tells you the total grams of all fat in each serving. It's then broken down into its component parts of saturated and unsaturated fats.

Saturated: This number tells you the total grams of saturated fat in each serving. Saturated fats are not essential fats. If you don't burn them for energy, your body stores them. These are fats you want to minimize in your foods.

Unsaturated: This number tells you the total grams of fat in the food that come from nonsaturated fats, such as monosaturated and polyunsaturated fatty acids. These fats are much better for you than saturated fats.

Cholesterol: This number is the total grams of cholesterol in each serving. Cholesterol is a component of every animal cell and no vegetables have cholesterol. It has been implicated as a factor in arteriosclerosis, or hardening of the arteries.

Sodium: This number is the total grams of sodium per serving. Try to minimize your sodium intake each day, and ideally, your potassium intake should be double your sodium intake.

Per Serving		
Total Fat	5	gm
Saturated	0.4	gm
Unsaturated	4.6	gm
Cholesterol	27	mg
Sodium	166	mg
Carbohydrate	442	gm
Protein	21	gm
Fiber	7	gm
Calories	297	

Carbohydrate: This number is the total grams of carbohydrates, both simple and complex, per serving.

Protein: This number is the total grams of protein in each serving. A diet rich in whole, unprocessed foods will give you all the proteins you need for growth and repair.

Fiber: This number is the total grams of fiber, both soluble and insoluble, in each serving. Soluble fibers are digestible carbohydrates that are burned as calories. Insoluble fibers are not burned as calories, but are important because they cleanse the digestive tract and keep sugars and excess fats from entering the bloodstream too rapidly. Eating a healthy diet of fruits, vegetables, beans, and grains will give you all the fiber you need.

Calories: This number shows the total calories in each serving. Don't agonize over counting every calorie you consume. But, if you're trying to lose weight, do exercise some portion control. To help you out with this, each recipe that follows indicates how many servings it will yield.

Notes

Cookbook Specials

Favorite Recipes

Dr. Whitaker's Favorite Recipes

Cabbage-Bean Soup (page 207)

Lasagna Florentine (page 126)

Lentil Stew (page 110)

Mineghetti Soup (page 211)

Rice Raffaele (page 112)

Spaghetti with Marinara Sauce (page 120)

Spicy Chili (page 108)

Traditional Split-Pea Soup (page 206)

Vegetable Tostada (page 147)

Kids' Favorite Recipes

Baked Apple with Lemon-Raisin Topping (page 238)

Banana Smoothie (page 57)

Carrot Sunshine Salad (page 87)

Enchiladas (page 161)

Monkey Milk (page 58)

Pizza (page 153)

Rice Pudding (page 240)

Stuffed Shells (page 124)

Lunch Box Favorite Recipes

Applesauce Muffins (page 242)

Banana Bread (page 247)

Corn Bread (page 246)

Engalian Pizzas (page 158)

Grilled Banana and Honey Sandwich (page 225)

Fruit Crisp (page 243)

Hummus Sandwich (page 225)

Munch Bowl (page 53)

Peach Cobbler (page 243)

Dinner Party Favorite Recipes

*Familiar foods with lots of flavor—simply multiply the
recipe according to the number of guests*

Baked Chicken and Pineapple (page 164)

Chef Salad (page 93)

Chicken and Vegetable Especiál (page 165)

Chicken Tetrazzini Casserole (page 139)

Fruit Punch (page 56)

Hot Apple Cider (page 55)

Munch Bowl (page 53)

Roast Chicken with Prune-Orange Stuffing (page 169)

Spinach-Stuffed Mushrooms (page 55)

Spinach-Mushroom Salad (page 89)

Stuffed Green Peppers with Rice and Sauce (page 149)

Tamale Pie (page 157)

Picnic Favorite Recipes

Crudités and Dip (page 52)

Delicious Pasta with Tuna (page 136)

Triple Bean Salad (page 91)

Munch Bowl (page 53)

Potato Salad (page 94)

Sesame Chicken Kabobs (page 170)

Fall Feast

Hot Apple Cider (page 55)
Black Bean Soup (page 205)
Roast Chicken with Prune-Orange Stuffing (page 169)
Mashed Potato Puff (page 192)
Baked Stuffed Butternut Squash (page 197)
Peach Cobbler (page 243)

Cozy Winter Supper

Curried Split-Pea Soup (page 206)
Basic Green Salad (page 92)
Buttermilk-Celery Seed Dressing (page 98)
Chicken Stroganoff (page 169)
Applesauce Cake (page 245)

Springtime Picnic

Fruit Punch (page 56)
Sprout Sandwiches (page 221)
Chicken Salad with Grapes (on whole grain bread) (page 164)
Broccoli and Bermuda Onion Salad (page 84)
Potato Salad (page 94)
Carob-Date Brownies (page 245)

Summer Seafood Delight

Lemon Cooler (page 56)
Sliced Tomato Salad (page 89)
Poached Salmon Veronique (page 179)
Pink Potatoes and Peas (page 193)
Orange Sherbet (page 241)

Country Inn Breakfast

Herbal Tea (store bought)
Cinnamon French Toast (page 67)
Fruit Salad (page 80)

Mexican Fiesta

Garbanzo Bean Dip (with low-fat tortilla chips) (page 54)
Gazpacho Soup (page 211)
Enchiladas (page 161)
Vegetable Tostadas (page 147)
Mexican Barley Supper (page 115)

Italian Surprise

Minestrone Soup (page 209)
Green Salad Romana (page 93)
Italian Dressing (page 99)
Linguini with Scallops (page 137)
Chopped Eggplant (page 52)

Chinese Choice

Chinese Salad (page 86)
Stir-Fry Vegetables with Ginger Sauce (page 146)
Oriental Noodles (page 148)

Fourth of July Barbecue

Jicama-Orange Salad (page 82)
Sesame Chicken Kabobs (page 170)
Vegetables in Mustard Vinaigrette (page 85)
Traditional Coleslaw (page 82)
Baked Beans (page 106)
Banana Smoothie (page 57)

Formal Dinner Gathering

Mushroom Paté (page 53)
Celery-Spinach Salad (page 88)
Rolled Filet of Sole (page 174)
Baked Rice and Peas Amandine (page 114)
Carob-Mint Mousse (page 239)

Appetizers, Beverages, & Snacks

Chopped Eggplant

Per Serving		
Total Fat	2	gm
Saturated	0.3	gm
Unsaturated	1.7	gm
Cholesterol	0	mg
Sodium	3	mg
Carbohydrate	7	gm
Protein	1	gm
Fiber	3	gm
Calories	50	

1 eggplant
1 medium onion
1 green pepper
1 T. olive oil
1 T. fresh lemon juice

1 t. red wine vinegar
¼ t. thyme
¼ t. pepper
Lettuce leaves, optional
Low-fat tortillas, optional

Preheat oven to 350° F. Bake whole eggplant until skin is soft and wrinkled. Remove from oven; cut skin away and discard. Chop eggplant and place into a large bowl. Finely chop onion and green pepper; add to chopped eggplant. Add oil, lemon juice, vinegar, thyme, and pepper. Mix well. Refrigerate. Serve in a mound on lettuce leaves with low-fat tortilla chips, if desired.
Prep. time: 30 min. *Serves 8.*

Crudités and Dip

Per Serving		
Total Fat	0.4	gm
Saturated	0.2	gm
Unsaturated	0.2	gm
Cholesterol	1	mg
Sodium	53	mg
Carbohydrate	8	gm
Protein	3	gm
Fiber	2	gm
Calories	43	

2 carrots, scraped, cut into 3-inch sticks
½ lb. green beans, washed, trimmed
1 c. broccoli florets
1 c. cauliflower florets

1 c. plain nonfat yogurt
½ t. Worcestershire sauce
½ t. prepared white horseradish
1 T. grated Parmesan cheese

Arrange vegetables on a platter. Keep in the refrigerator until ready to serve. For the dip, combine yogurt, Worcestershire sauce, horseradish, and grated Parmesan cheese. Place in center of vegetable platter.
Prep. time: 15 min. *Serves 8.*

Munch Bowl

4 c. fresh air-popped corn
1 c. seedless raisins
2 c. puffed wheat cereal

½ c. hulled sunflower seeds
½ t. ground cinnamon

Per Serving		
Total Fat	3	gm
Saturated	0.3	gm
Unsaturated	2.7	gm
Cholesterol	0	mg
Sodium	2	mg
Carbohydrate	12	gm
Protein	2	gm
Fiber	1	gm
Calories	74	

Combine all ingredients and mix well.
Prep. time: 10 min. *Makes 15 ½-cup servings.*

Mushroom Paté

5 c. mushrooms, finely diced
2 brown onions, diced fine
2 cloves garlic, diced
3 T. water

2-3 t. allspice
½ t. garlic powder
1 t. basil
2-3 T. arrowroot, cornstarch or whole wheat flour

Per Serving		
Total Fat	0.3	gm
Saturated	0	gm
Unsaturated	0.3	gm
Cholesterol	0	mg
Sodium	5	mg
Carbohydrate	10	gm
Protein	2	gm
Fiber	2	gm
Calories	46	

In large cast-iron skillet, sauté the mushrooms, onions, and garlic in water until well cooked (soft). Add the spices and mix well. Add arrowroot, cornstarch, or whole wheat flour to thicken. Allow mixture to cool. May be formed for fancy dip arrangement.
Prep. time: 25 min. *Serves 8.*

Garbanzo Bean Dip

Per Serving

Total Fat	2	gm
Saturated	0	gm
Unsaturated	2	gm
Cholesterol	0	mg
Sodium	17	mg
Carbohydrate	26	gm
Protein	9	gm
Fiber	1	gm
Calories	152	

2 c. garbanzo beans

1 stalk celery, diced fine

¼ c. fresh parsley, diced fine

1-2 tomatoes, diced fine

1 clove garlic

1 t. cumin

½ t. garlic powder

¼ t. cayenne pepper

Diced fresh mint, optional

10 pieces of pita bread cut into triangles, optional

Cook garbanzo beans until done. Purée cooked beans in a blender or food processor. Add remaining ingredients. Blend well. Serve with pita bread, if desired.

Prep. time: 50 min. *Makes 10 2½-cup servings.*

Garbanzo beans (also called chickpeas) contain protease inhibitors. Proteases are protein-splitting enzymes necessary for normal biological functions. However, to survive, cancer cells need proteases. A diet rich in garbanzo and other beans can supply protease inhibitors, which may protect against cell proliferation as seen in cancer.

Spinach-Stuffed Mushrooms

1 package (10 oz.) frozen
chopped spinach,
thawed

12 large mushrooms
(2-inch diameter)

1 T. chopped fresh
parsley

⅛ t. pepper

⅛ t. ground nutmeg

¼ c. wheat germ

Per Serving		
Total Fat	1	gm
Saturated	0.2	gm
Unsaturated	0.8	gm
Cholesterol	0	mg
Sodium	42	mg
Carbohydrate	8	gm
Protein	4	gm
Fiber	2	gm
Calories	51	

Preheat oven to 350° F. Drain thawed spinach in a
strainer and press out all excess moisture. Wash
mushrooms and carefully remove stems. Chop stems
and place in mixing bowl. Chop spinach and combine
with chopped stems. Add parsley, pepper, and
nutmeg. Mix well and stuff mixture into mushroom
caps. Place mushrooms, stuffing side up, in a small
baking dish. Top each with a teaspoon of wheat
germ. Bake for 15 min.
Prep. time: 35 min. *Serves 4.*

Hot Apple Cider

1 gallon unsweetened
apple cider or apple
juice

1 t. whole cloves

4 cinnamon sticks

1 t. whole allspice

Per Serving		
Total Fat	0.3	gm
Saturated	0.1	gm
Unsaturated	0.2	gm
Cholesterol	0	mg
Sodium	8	mg
Carbohydrate	35	gm
Protein	0.3	gm
Fiber	0.2	gm
Calories	125	

Warm apple cider or juice on medium heat for
10 min. Add spices. Simmer on low heat an
additional 10 min. Strain out the spices. Serve hot.
Prep. time: 23 min. *Makes 16 1-cup servings.*

Fruit Punch

Per Serving

Total Fat	0.1	gm
Saturated	0	gm
Unsaturated	0.1	gm
Cholesterol	0	mg
Sodium	12	mg
Carbohydrate	15	gm
Protein	1	gm
Fiber	0.3	gm
Calories	61	

This delightful punch is less expensive than those bottled sparkling juices, and it's a very healthy alternative to colas.

1 pint berry juice or grape juice

4 c. orange juice

½ c. lemon juice

1 pint club soda

Fresh orange, lemon, and lime slices, optional

Frozen fruit juice ice cubes, optional

Mix juices and club soda together. Decorate with citrus fruit slices. Serve cold. Optional: Instead of citrus fruit slices, float frozen fruit juice ice cubes in the punch bowl.
Prep. time: 5 min. *Makes 12 1-cup servings.*

Lemon Cooler

Per Serving

Total Fat	0.3	gm
Saturated	0	gm
Unsaturated	0.3	gm
Cholesterol	0	mg
Sodium	8	mg
Carbohydrate	36	gm
Protein	0.4	gm
Fiber	1	gm
Calories	140	

2 c. apple juice

¼ c. fresh lemon juice

1 T. thawed frozen pineapple juice concentrate

Blend ingredients and serve ice cold.
Prep. time: 5 min. *Serves 2.*

Banana Smoothie

Frozen bananas make rich, thick shakes that taste and feel like frozen yogurt shakes—without the dairy products in them.

1 c. orange juice

1 ripe, peeled banana

3 pitted dates

Ice cubes, optional

Per Serving		
Total Fat	1	gm
Saturated	0.3	gm
Unsaturated	0.7	gm
Cholesterol	0	mg
Sodium	4	mg
Carbohydrate	71	gm
Protein	3	gm
Fiber	5	gm
Calories	282	

Blend orange juice with banana and dates until thick. Serve cold. For a thicker, richer, colder drink, freeze the ripe peeled banana first. Or use ¾ c. orange juice and add several ice cubes while blending.
Prep. time: 5 min. *Serves 1.*

Tomato Juice Cocktail

1 pint water

1 can unsalted tomato paste

1 pint mixed fresh vegetable juices (carrot, celery, parsley, beet)

4 T. vinegar

2 T. lemon juice

2 T. vegetable broth powder

Sprig of parsley or mint for garnish, optional

Per Serving		
Total Fat	2	gm
Saturated	0.1	gm
Unsaturated	1.9	gm
Cholesterol	0	mg
Sodium	66	mg
Carbohydrate	22	gm
Protein	4	gm
Fiber	5	gm
Calories	109	

Blend all ingredients except garnish; chill. Shake well before serving. Garnish with parsley or mint, if desired.
Prep. time: 5 min. *Serves 4.*

Lemon Froth

Per Serving

Total Fat	0.3	gm
Saturated	0.1	gm
Unsaturated	0.1	gm
Cholesterol	0	mg
Sodium	8	mg
Carbohydrate	35	gm
Protein	0.3	gm
Fiber	0.2	gm
Calories	125	

½ c. plain nonfat yogurt

Juice of ½ lemon

1 T. pure maple syrup or honey

1 c. crushed ice *or* ½ c. cold water and 4 ice cubes

Blend ingredients and serve immediately.
Prep. time: 2 min. *Serves 2.*

Monkey Milk

Per Serving

Total Fat	1	gm
Saturated	0.5	gm
Unsaturated	0.5	gm
Cholesterol	5	mg
Sodium	147	mg
Carbohydrate	42	gm
Protein	11	gm
Fiber	2	gm
Calories	213	

1 c. nonfat milk

2 T. plain nonfat yogurt

½ t. vanilla

1 large ripe banana

Blend all together. Serve ice cold.
Prep. time: 5 min. *Serves 1.*

Breakfast

Spanish Omelet

Per Serving

Total Fat	0.1	gm
Saturated	0	gm
Unsaturated	0.1	gm
Cholesterol	1	mg
Sodium	138	mg
Carbohydrate	6	gm
Protein	9	gm
Fiber	1	gm
Calories	62	

¼ c. unsalted tomato purée

⅛ c. water

¼ t. onion flakes

Pepper to taste

4 egg whites

4 T. nonfat milk

1 T. nonfat yogurt

⅛ t. pepper

Make the sauce by combining the first 4 ingredients and simmering over low heat for 10 min. While sauce is simmering, whip together the egg whites, milk, yogurt, and pepper in a blender. On a non-stick pan coated with nonfat cooking spray, cook egg mixture over medium heat until the bottom is brown and the top is set. Fill with half the sauce, fold the omelet, and spoon the other half of the sauce over the top.

Prep. time: 20 min. *Serves 2.*

Cottage Cheese Omelet

Per Serving

Total Fat	1	gm
Saturated	0.4	gm
Unsaturated	0.6	gm
Cholesterol	3	mg
Sodium	422	mg
Carbohydrate	3	gm
Protein	19	gm
Fiber	0.1	gm
Calories	98	

There's no law that says you can't cheat and add a pinch of tumeric to color your egg whites yellow. We do at the Institute. It's amazing how sight can influence taste!

3 egg whites

¼ t. tumeric

¼ t. dried dill weed

¼ c. 1% low-fat cottage cheese

½ t. chopped chives

Dash pepper

Beat egg whites and tumeric lightly with a fork until foamy. Add dill weed. Pour into a non-stick skillet. Cook over medium heat until whites are almost solidified. Spoon cottage cheese over half the omelet, cover with other half. Roll out onto a plate. Sprinkle with chopped chives and a dusting of pepper.

Prep. time: 15 min. *Serves 1.*

Western Omelet

1 small tomato, diced

½ yellow onion, chopped

1 zucchini, sliced and quartered

4 oz. fresh mushrooms, sliced

1 slice green pepper, chopped

1 t. olive oil

2 T. mild chile salsa

1 t. vegetable broth seasoning

⅛ t. black pepper

4 egg whites

4 pieces whole grain bread, toasted

Per Serving		
Total Fat	5	gm
Saturated	0.4	gm
Unsaturated	4.6	gm
Cholesterol	0	mg
Sodium	598	mg
Carbohydrate	39	gm
Protein	16	gm
Fiber	9	gm
Calories	253	

In a non-stick skillet, sauté the tomato, onion, zucchini, mushrooms, and green pepper. Add oil, salsa, seasoning, and pepper. While the mixture simmers, beat egg whites with a fork and pour onto the mixture, stirring while it cooks to keep it from sticking. (Use a utensil safe for non-stick surfaces.) Cook until the egg sets. Spoon over toast.
Prep. time: 30 min. *Serves 2.*

Swiss-Style Muesli

1 c. uncooked oatmeal

1 apple, peeled and shredded

¼ c. raisins

2 T. almonds, slivered

2 T. dried apricots, chopped

1 ¼ c. fresh pineapple juice *or* nonfat milk, optional

Per Serving		
Total Fat	7	gm
Saturated	0.9	gm
Unsaturated	6.1	gm
Cholesterol	0	mg
Sodium	6	mg
Carbohydrate	59	gm
Protein	9	gm
Fiber	7	gm
Calories	312	

Mix ingredients together and eat immediately. It will be chewy and dry. For a more moist mixture, soak ingredients overnight in fresh pineapple juice or nonfat milk. Keep refrigerated.
Prep. time: 5 min. *Serves 2.*

Special Oatmeal

Per Serving

Total Fat	3	gm
Saturated	0.6	gm
Unsaturated	2.4	gm
Cholesterol	0	mg
Sodium	13	mg
Carbohydrate	55	gm
Protein	7	gm
Fiber	3	gm
Calories	267	

1 c. uncooked oatmeal
2 c. boiling water
1 large ripe banana, mashed

1 c. apple juice

Stir the oatmeal into the boiling water. Cook for 3 to 5 min., depending upon the texture you prefer. Remove from heat. Put half of mashed banana in each of two serving bowls. Pour oatmeal into bowls over banana. Pour apple juice over oatmeal. Prep. time: 10 min. *Serves 2.*

High-Fiber Granola

Per Serving

Total Fat	16	gm
Saturated	2.7	gm
Unsaturated	13.3	gm
Cholesterol	0	mg
Sodium	14	mg
Carbohydrate	107	gm
Protein	16	gm
Fiber	11	gm
Calories	597	

½ c. oatmeal
½ c. oat bran
2 T. honey
1 T. water
¼ c. chopped dates or date pieces

⅛ c. unhulled sesame seeds
⅛ c. chopped cashews
2 t. olive oil
½ c. raisins

Preheat oven to 350° F. Toast the oatmeal and oat bran together on a large, dry cookie sheet for 10 min. Mix honey and water together. Toss the honey mixture with the dates, sesame seeds, and cashews. Add the oats mixture. Spread mixture onto a cookie sheet coated with nonfat cooking spray. Return to oven and bake for 20 min. more, stirring every few minutes. Remove from oven and transfer to a mixing bowl. Add oil and raisins. Mix well. Cool and serve. Prep. time: 50 min. *Serves 2.*

Cinnamon-Raisin Oatmeal

1 ¾ c. water
¾ c. oatmeal
¾ t. cinnamon

¼ c. raisins
½ c. apple juice *or*
   nonfat milk, optional

Per Serving		
Total Fat	2	gm
Saturated	0.4	gm
Unsaturated	1.6	gm
Cholesterol	0	mg
Sodium	10	mg
Carbohydrate	35	gm
Protein	6	gm
Fiber	2	gm
Calories	173	

Bring water to a boil. Stir in oatmeal and cook for
5 min. Add cinnamon and raisins; remove from heat.
Serve as is or, for more moist oatmeal, serve with
apple juice or nonfat milk.
Prep. time: 10 min. *Serves 2.*

Carob Hot Cereal

2 ¼ c. water
1 c. oatmeal
1 T. unsweetened carob
   powder

½ t. cinnamon
1 T. raisins
2 t. honey

Per Serving		
Total Fat	3	gm
Saturated	0.5	gm
Unsaturated	2.5	gm
Cholesterol	0	mg
Sodium	13	mg
Carbohydrate	42	gm
Protein	7	gm
Fiber	2	gm
Calories	205	

Bring the water to a boil. Stir in the oatmeal, carob
powder, and cinnamon. Cook for 3 min. Remove
from heat and stir in the raisins and honey. Let stand
covered for 1 min. No need to add any milk or
juice—it's delicious as is!
Prep. time: 10 min. *Serves 2.*

*Carob, also called St. John's Bread, is naturally
sweet and doesn't have any caffeine in it—unlike
chocolate. In fact, it's a very rich source of vitamins and
minerals, so enjoy it.*

Crockpot Oatmeal with Apricot

Per Serving

Total Fat	2	gm
Saturated	0.3	gm
Unsaturated	1.7	gm
Cholesterol	0	mg
Sodium	9	mg
Carbohydrate	40	gm
Protein	5	gm
Fiber	4	gm
Calories	193	

We think of millet as the "King of Grains." It's good if you're gluten-intolerant, it's easy to find, and it tastes great—especially in this terrific breakfast cereal.

1 ¼ c. water
½ c. oatmeal
½ c. apple juice

¼ c. chopped dried apricots
⅛ c. millet

Put all the ingredients into a crockpot and leave on low approximately 8 hours. Check the crockpot mixture periodically and add water if needed.
Prep. time: 8 hours. *Serves 2.*

Apple-Corn Muffins

Per Serving

Total Fat	2	gm
Saturated	0.3	gm
Unsaturated	1.7	gm
Cholesterol	0	mg
Sodium	21	mg
Carbohydrate	21	gm
Protein	3	gm
Fiber	2	gm
Calories	108	

¾ c. whole wheat flour
⅓ c. yellow cornmeal
1 T. baking powder
¼ c. finely grated apple
2 egg whites, stiffly beaten

½ c. apple juice
1 T. olive oil
¼ c. puréed date, or date "sugar"

Preheat oven to 375° F. Sift first three ingredients together. Add apple, beaten egg whites, apple juice, and olive oil. Stir in date purée or date "sugar." Pour muffin mixture into muffin pans coated with nonfat cooking spray. Fill the pans only two-thirds full and bake for 20 min. until done.
Prep. time: 25 min. *Makes 8 muffins.*

Corn Fritters

2 egg whites, stiffly
  beaten

½ c. nonfat milk

½ c. whole wheat flour

1 c. frozen corn, soaked
  with a little water, then
  drained

1 t. chopped chives

¼ c. minced onions

½ t. basil

Per Serving		
Total Fat	1	gm
Saturated	0.1	gm
Unsaturated	0.9	gm
Cholesterol	0.3	mg
Sodium	31	mg
Carbohydrate	16	gm
Protein	4	gm
Fiber	1	gm
Calories	78	

Preheat oven to 375° F. Combine beaten egg whites
and milk. Stir in the whole wheat flour to make batter.
Add rest of the ingredients and drop by spoonfuls onto
preheated non-stick pan or baking sheet. Cook on top
of range or bake in oven until lightly browned. Turn
over and brown the other side.
Prep. time: 35 min. *Serves 2.*

Cinnamon French Toast

*This is a hearty, healthy breakfast that's especially
good with applesauce or a mashed banana on top.*

1 egg white

½ c. skim milk

½ t. vanilla extract

4 slices whole grain
  bread

Dash of cinnamon

Per Serving		
Total Fat	3	gm
Saturated	0.1	gm
Unsaturated	2.9	gm
Cholesterol	1	mg
Sodium	415	mg
Carbohydrate	29	gm
Protein	9	gm
Fiber	6	gm
Calories	171	

Beat egg white until frothy. Add skim milk and
vanilla extract. Dip bread slices into the batter, one at
a time, coating each side well. Place on a hot, non-
stick griddle or skillet. Cook over medium heat until
browned on one side, then turn and brown the other
side. Place onto serving plates and sprinkle lightly
with cinnamon.
Prep. time: 10 min. *Serves 2.*

Orange Pancakes with Orange Sauce

½ c. orange juice

¼ c. liquid Butter Buds

1 egg white

1 T. orange juice
  concentrate

½ c. whole wheat flour

1 ½ t. baking powder

2 T. ground nuts or seeds
  (sunflower or sesame
  seeds, almonds,
  walnuts, or pecans)

2 t. olive oil

Blend all ingredients in a blender, adding the dry
ingredients slowly until mixture has the consistency
of pancake batter. Bake on a hot non-stick griddle. Serve
with Orange Sauce (see recipe below).
Prep. time: 20 min. *Serves 2.*

Orange Sauce

*Arrowroot is from the root of the cassava plant. When
you want a clear sauce, use it as a thickener. It's usually
only available in health food stores, but the health food
aisle of your grocery store might have it, too.*

¼ c. orange juice

1 thin slice orange

1 T. arrowroot
  (cornstarch can be
  substituted)

2 T. honey

Combine orange juice, orange slice, and arrowroot in
a double boiler and cook, stirring, until thick. Remove
from heat and stir in honey.
Prep. time: 15 min. *Serves 2.*

*In England, the Tuesday before Ash Wednesday is
known as "Pancake Tuesday," because of an old custom
that involved eating pancakes. It seems the English
designated this day to use up all the fat in the house before
the commencement of the Lenten season, when no fat was
eaten. The same day is known as "Mardi Gras" or "Fat
Tuesday" in the United States.*

Oatmeal-Raisin Pancakes

1 c. unbleached flour

½ c. uncooked oatmeal

1 T. baking powder

1 c. skim milk

2 egg whites

1 T. olive oil

1 t. vanilla extract

¼ c. seedless raisins

1 c. puréed berries, optional

Per Serving		
Total Fat	3	gm
Saturated	0.5	gm
Unsaturated	2.5	gm
Cholesterol	1	mg
Sodium	49	mg
Carbohydrate	28	gm
Protein	6	gm
Fiber	1	gm
Calories	165	

Combine flour, oatmeal, and baking powder. Add milk, egg whites, olive oil, and vanilla extract. Add raisins. Stir until mixed through. Spoon ¼ c. of batter onto a non-stick griddle. Repeat until all batter is used. Cook on medium heat. Turn over when browned on underside. Serve at once with puréed berries as a topping, if desired.
Prep. time: 25 min. Makes 12 pancakes. *Serves 6.*

We all know that oat fiber can help lower cholesterol, but did you know that common oats have been used successfully in India to treat opium addiction?

Whole Wheat Pancakes

2 ½ c. whole wheat
pastry flour

1 ½ t. baking powder

¼ c. olive oil

2 c. skim milk

4 egg whites

Walnuts, bananas, or
blueberries, optional

Per Serving		
Total Fat	15	gm
Saturated	2	gm
Unsaturated	13	gm
Cholesterol	2	mg
Sodium	128	mg
Carbohydrate	61	gm
Protein	18	gm
Fiber	9	gm
Calories	436	

Combine dry ingredients. Add olive oil, milk, and egg whites. When mixed well, pour onto a non-stick griddle or waffle iron. Add walnuts, bananas, or blueberries for a change.
Prep. time: 10 min. *Serves 4.*

Carrot Waffles

Per Serving

Total Fat	5	gm
Saturated	0.8	gm
Unsaturated	4.2	gm
Cholesterol	0	mg
Sodium	73	mg
Carbohydrate	51	gm
Protein	10	gm
Fiber	6	gm
Calories	280	

The hardest thing to do is to get children to eat what's good for them, like carrots for beta-carotene. The easiest thing to do is to get kids to eat what tastes good, like waffles—but don't tell the kids these are good for them.

½ c. apple juice

¼ c. chopped carrots

2 t. olive oil

1 T. honey

1 t. baking powder

¾ c. whole wheat flour

2 egg whites, stiffly beaten

Blend apple juice and chopped carrots together. While the blender is running, add olive oil, honey, and baking powder. Pour into a bowl and mix in the whole wheat flour. Fold in beaten egg whites. Bake on a non-stick waffle iron. Serve with Butter Buds and applesauce or fruit syrup, if desired. Prep. time: 22 min. *Serves 2.*

Oat Bran Waffles

Per Serving

Total Fat	9	gm
Saturated	1.4	gm
Unsaturated	7.6	gm
Cholesterol	0	mg
Sodium	42	mg
Carbohydrate	60	gm
Protein	13	gm
Fiber	10	gm
Calories	348	

1 c. water

1 ripe banana

1 egg white

1 t. baking powder

1 T. olive oil

½ t. vanilla

¾ c. whole wheat flour

½ c. oat bran

Put all ingredients into a blender, except wheat flour and oat bran. Blend. While the blender is running, add flour and bran, a little at a time. Cook on a medium-hot non-stick waffle iron. Serve with Butter Buds and applesauce or fruit syrup, if desired. Prep. time: 15 min. *Serves 2.*

Plain Wheat Pancakes

1 c. soured nonfat milk

2 egg whites, stiffly
beaten

1 c. whole wheat flour

1 t. baking powder

½ t. baking soda

Per Serving		
Total Fat	1	gm
Saturated	0.3	gm
Unsaturated	0.7	gm
Cholesterol	2	mg
Sodium	335	mg
Carbohydrate	51	gm
Protein	16	gm
Fiber	8	gm
Calories	267	

Blend all ingredients in a blender and cook on a
non-stick pan.
Prep. time: 12 min. *Serves 2.*

Oatmeal Pancakes

1 ½ c. old-fashioned
rolled oats

1 c. nonfat milk

1 t. lemon juice

1 t. vanilla

½ c. whole wheat pastry
flour

1 t. baking soda

2 egg whites, stiffly
beaten

Per Serving		
Total Fat	2	gm
Saturated	0.5	gm
Unsaturated	1.5	gm
Cholesterol	1	mg
Sodium	268	mg
Carbohydrate	38	gm
Protein	11	gm
Fiber	3	gm
Calories	216	

Blend oats in food processor or blender. Add liquids
and let stand 5 min. Add remaining dry ingredients.
Fold in egg whites. Cook pancakes on a non-stick
pan.
Prep. time: 20 min. *Serves 4.*

Oatmeal-Cinnamon Pancakes

Per Serving

Total Fat	4	gm
Saturated	0.8	gm
Unsaturated	3.2	gm
Cholesterol	3	mg
Sodium	110	mg
Carbohydrate	72	gm
Protein	19	gm
Fiber	6	gm
Calories	392	

½ c. whole wheat flour
1 ¼ c. oatmeal (put in blender or food processor to process)
1 ¼ c. skim milk
1 T. honey
½ t. cinnamon
1 egg white, beaten

Combine flour, oatmeal, and milk. Add honey and cinnamon. Fold in egg white. Cook on a hot non-stick griddle.
Prep. time: 15 min. *Serves 2.*

Belgian Waffles

Per Serving

Total Fat	1	gm
Saturated	0.3	gm
Unsaturated	0.7	gm
Cholesterol	2	mg
Sodium	135	mg
Carbohydrate	50	gm
Protein	17	gm
Fiber	8	gm
Calories	268	

2 c. whole wheat flour
2 c. nonfat milk
5 egg whites, beaten

Mix flour with milk. Fold in stiffly beaten egg whites. Bake in Belgian waffle iron.
Prep. time: 15 min. *Serves 4.*

Strawberry Syrup

Be prepared to double and triple this recipe. This homemade syrup is sweeter than just using applesauce, yet not sugary-sweet like most store-bought syrups.

½ c. mashed strawberries

½ c. apple juice

2 t. tapioca granules

1 T. honey

Per Serving		
Total Fat	0.2	gm
Saturated	0	gm
Unsaturated	0.2	gm
Cholesterol	0	mg
Sodium	3	mg
Carbohydrate	21	gm
Protein	0.3	gm
Fiber	1	gm
Calories	83	

Combine ingredients and cook in a saucepan, bringing to a bubble and stirring constantly. Remove from heat and let cool until warm. Prep. time: 15 min. *Makes 1 cup.*

Blueberry Spread

2 c. unsweetened frozen blueberries

2 T. honey

1 t. vanilla

Pinch of nutmeg

Per Serving		
Total Fat	0.3	gm
Saturated	0.1	gm
Unsaturated	0.2	gm
Cholesterol	0	mg
Sodium	5	mg
Carbohydrate	19	gm
Protein	1	gm
Fiber	2	gm
Calories	76	

Heat and simmer blueberries in saucepan. Remove from heat; stir in honey, vanilla, and nutmeg. Serve warm, over waffles, pancakes, or cereal. Prep. time: 15 min. *Makes 2 cups.*

Banana Topping

1 ½ c. nonfat milk 1 ½ t. vanilla

2 medium bananas

Blend ingredients together. Use over fruit, cereal, pancakes, or waffles.

Prep. time: 5 min. *Serves 2.*

Breakfast Bars

½ c. apple juice

1 small banana

1 egg white

½ t. lemon extract

½ t. cinnamon

1 T. honey

½ c. oat bran

1 T. baking powder

2 ½ oz. whole, pitted dates (approx. ½ c.)

3 fresh apricots, pitted (1 ½ inches in diameter)

1 t. vanilla

Preheat oven to 350° F. Combine the first eight ingredients in the blender. Pour the mixture into a non-stick 10 x 10-inch baking dish. Bake for 30 min. While mixture is baking, blend dates, apricots, and vanilla in a blender. You may need to stop the blender and press the mixture away from the blades a few times, as it is sticky. Top the bars with the blended mixture after 30 min., and bake 10 min. more at 400° F.

Prep. time: 50 min. *Serves 4.*

Yummy Yeast Drink

1 c. fruit juice (any one you like)

1 ripe banana

1 t. brewer's yeast

½ c. (handful) of frozen fruit—blueberries, peaches, strawberries, or any kind you like, optional

Per Serving		
Total Fat	1	gm
Saturated	0.2	gm
Unsaturated	0.8	gm
Cholesterol	0	mg
Sodium	7	mg
Carbohydrate	60	gm
Protein	4	gm
Fiber	5	gm
Calories	248	

Blend ingredients until smooth. Serve immediately. Note: You can use anywhere between 1 t. and 4 heaping T. of brewer's yeast for this recipe. But beware, yeast can cause gas. Let your body adjust to the yeast intake by starting with 1 t. in your drink and gradually increasing the amount, as desired. Prep. time: 5 min. *Serves 2 as a snack or 1 as a meal.*

Papaya Fruit Smoothie

Juice of ½ lemon

1 c. cubed papaya

½ c. plain nonfat yogurt

1 T. pure maple syrup

½ c. crushed ice

1 T. brewer's yeast, optional

Per Serving		
Total Fat	0.2	gm
Saturated	0.1	gm
Unsaturated	0.1	gm
Cholesterol	3	mg
Sodium	88	mg
Carbohydrate	50	gm
Protein	8	gm
Fiber	1	gm
Calories	219	

Blend ingredients and serve immediately. Prep. time: 5 min. *Serves 2 as a snack or 1 as a meal.*

The Fruit Smoothies in this cookbook give you a delightful way to turn fresh fruits into a satisfying meal. The variations are endless. Use your imagination and the fruits in season for a rich supply of vitamins and raw enzymes along with nutritious yeast. Here are a few winning combinations.

Spring Fruit Smoothie

Per Serving

Total Fat	7	gm
Saturated	1.7	gm
Unsaturated	5.3	gm
Cholesterol	0	mg
Sodium	3	mg
Carbohydrate	24	gm
Protein	1	gm
Fiber	3	gm
Calories	141	

Lecithin is important for optimum brain and liver functions. This Smoothie is one of the most pleasant ways to make lecithin part of your day.

½ c. frozen blueberries   1 frozen ripe banana

1 ripe peach   1 T. lecithin

½ c. filtered water   1 T. brewer's yeast, optional

Blend ingredients and serve immediately.
Prep. time: 5 min. *Serves 2 as a snack or 1 as a meal.*

Tropical Fruit Smoothie

Per Serving

Total Fat	1	gm
Saturated	0.2	gm
Unsaturated	0.8	gm
Cholesterol	0	mg
Sodium	6	mg
Carbohydrate	45	gm
Protein	2	gm
Fiber	4	gm
Calories	176	

1 fresh mango   ½ c. apple or pineapple juice

1 frozen very ripe banana

1 c. papaya cubes   1 T. yeast and 1 T. lecithin, optional

Blend ingredients and serve immediately.
Prep. time: 5 min. *Serves 2 as a snack or 1 as a meal.*

Barley with Fruit Breakfast Pudding

1 c. cooked barley

2 T. honey

¼ c. apple juice

½ c. diced apples

⅛ t. nutmeg

¼ t. cinnamon

½ t. vanilla

2 T. raisins

1 T. chopped raw walnuts

Per Serving		
Total Fat	2	gm
Saturated	0.2	gm
Unsaturated	1.8	gm
Cholesterol	0	mg
Sodium	6	mg
Carbohydrate	56	gm
Protein	3	gm
Fiber	6	gm
Calories	243	

Preheat oven to 350° F. Mix all ingredients except walnuts together and pour into a non-stick casserole dish. Bake for 30 min. Add walnuts before serving.
Prep. time: 45 min. *Serves 2.*

Potato Pancakes

These are great in the morning on the side of a piping hot omelet. Try it!

1 c. water

1 egg white

1 T. honey

2 t. olive oil

1 t. vanilla

1 c. chopped, unpeeled potato (1 small potato)

½ c. corn flour

¼ c. oat bran

1 T. baking powder

1 ½ c. oatmeal

Per Serving		
Total Fat	5	gm
Saturated	0.8	gm
Unsaturated	4.2	gm
Cholesterol	0	mg
Sodium	34	mg
Carbohydrate	50	gm
Protein	9	gm
Fiber	5	gm
Calories	276	

Blend the ingredients together in a blender in the order listed. Bake on a hot, non-stick griddle or waffle iron. Serve with Butter Buds, unsweetened fruit syrup or honey, and applesauce on the side, if desired.
Prep. time: 15 min. *Serves 4.*

Salads & Salad Dressings

Fruit Salad

Per Serving

Total Fat	1	gm
Saturated	0.1	gm
Unsaturated	0.9	gm
Cholesterol	0	mg
Sodium	2	mg
Carbohydrate	41	gm
Protein	2	gm
Fiber	5	gm
Calories	159	

1 ripe banana, thinly sliced

1 c. stone fruits, pitted and cut into chunks (peaches, apricots, nectarines, etc.)

1 c. seasonal fruits (strawberries, melon, kiwi, papaya, oranges, etc.)

½ c. pineapple chunks

Combine all ingredients in a bowl.
Prep. time: 20 min. *Serves 2.*

Fruit Gelatin

Per Serving

Total Fat	0.3	gm
Saturated	0	gm
Unsaturated	0.3	gm
Cholesterol	1	mg
Sodium	30	mg
Carbohydrate	31	gm
Protein	4	gm
Fiber	1	gm
Calories	134	

1 ¾ c. fruit juice

¼ c. thawed frozen orange juice concentrate

1 package unflavored gelatin

1 large ripe banana

2 ½ c. crushed unsweetened pineapple

8 oz. nonfat yogurt

Bring the fruit juice to a boil and stir in the orange juice concentrate. Pour dry gelatin into a large bowl; add hot juice mixture until gelatin is completely dissolved. Refrigerate until slightly thickened. Blend banana, pineapple, and yogurt. Mix gelatin mixture with blended mixture until smooth or chunky, as you desire. Pour into a 2-quart mold or individual molds. Chill until set.
Prep. time: 40 min. *Serves 6.*

Gelatin is an animal source protein taken from the skin and bones of animals. Unlike meat, fish, eggs, and milk, which contain all the essential amino acids, gelatin lacks tryptophan, and would therefore be unable to support growth if consumed as the sole source of protein. Eating a diet containing a variety of whole vegetable foods, however, provides all the amino acids you need for growth and repair.

Apple Salad

1 peeled, cored, and cubed red apple, peeling optional

1 peeled, cored, and cubed green apple, peeling optional

1 peeled, cored, and cubed yellow apple, peeling optional

½ c. seedless raisins

¼ c. chopped unblanched almonds

Fruit Salad Dressing of your choice (see pages 96-97)

Per Serving		
Total Fat	5	gm
Saturated	0.5	gm
Unsaturated	4.5	gm
Cholesterol	1	mg
Sodium	34	mg
Carbohydrate	50	gm
Protein	5	gm
Fiber	5	gm
Calories	240	

Combine all ingredients and serve with enough dressing to moisten thoroughly.
Prep. time: 10 min. *Serves 4.*

Zesty Coleslaw

1 package no-oil salad dressing mix

½ head shredded cabbage (or mix purple with green)

2 large shredded carrots

1 small chopped green pepper

2 chopped scallions

¼ t. garlic powder

1 T. celery seed

1 t. mustard powder

1 c. plain nonfat yogurt

Per Serving		
Total Fat	1	gm
Saturated	0	gm
Unsaturated	1	gm
Cholesterol	1	mg
Sodium	114	mg
Carbohydrate	19	gm
Protein	7	gm
Fiber	5	gm
Calories	104	

Prepare salad dressing, using recommended amount of vinegar. Combine with other ingredients. Mix and refrigerate overnight.
Prep. time: 40 min. *Serves 4.*

Cabbage is an excellent source of vitamin K, which is required for the synthesis of prothrombin, the precursor of thrombin, which prevents hemorrhaging.

Jicama-Orange Salad

Jicama is a crunchy, slightly sweet, watery vegetable that is quite common in grocery stores. Peel the outer skin back to get to the edible part. If you wish, you can use apples instead. But try jicama. There really is no substitute, and you may end up loving it. We do.

Dressing:

¼ c. vinegar
1 T. flax oil
2 t. vegetable broth seasoning
⅛ t. white pepper
⅛ t. chili powder
1 clove garlic, peeled and halved
1 t. honey

Salad:

3 navel oranges, peeled and sectioned
2 sweet red peppers cut into thin strips
1 small jicama cut into matchstick strips (discard the brown part and any fibrous portions)
Lime wedges for garnish

Combine the dressing ingredients in a jar with a tight fitting lid. Shake vigorously. Let stand overnight (or as long as possible) to combine flavors. Toss the dressing together with the salad ingredients just before serving. Garnish with lime wedges. Variation: Add other tropical fruits, or cut-up apple pieces.
Prep. time: 20 min., plus standing time. *Serves 4.*

Traditional Coleslaw

6 T. nonfat yogurt
2 T. lemon juice
1 T. nonfat milk

½ t. dill seed
1 head cabbage, finely shredded

Blend yogurt, lemon juice, milk, and dill seed. Mix with shredded cabbage.
Prep. time: 30 min. *Serves 8.*

Beet Salad

2 c. julienne beets

2 t. flax oil

1 c. red onion, thinly sliced

1 T. chopped parsley

1 T. vegetable broth seasoning

3 T. vinegar

Per Serving		
Total Fat	3	gm
Saturated	0.2	gm
Unsaturated	2.8	gm
Cholesterol	0	mg
Sodium	91	mg
Carbohydrate	18	gm
Protein	3	gm
Fiber	5	gm
Calories	98	

Toss all ingredients together; marinate 1 hour. If salad becomes too dry, add 1 t. more flax oil. Prep. time: 1 hour and 10 min. *Serves 4.*

Fresh Broccoli Salad

1 head fresh broccoli, broken into florets (may substitute 10 oz. package frozen broccoli spears)

¼ c. diagonally cut celery

½ c. Italian dressing (no salt, no oil)

¼ c. orange juice

Pinch dill weed

1 orange, peeled and sectioned

3 hard-boiled eggs (whites only)

Salad greens

Per Serving		
Total Fat	0.4	gm
Saturated	0	gm
Unsaturated	0.4	gm
Cholesterol	0	mg
Sodium	166	mg
Carbohydrate	23	gm
Protein	11	gm
Fiber	6	gm
Calories	126	

Steam broccoli until tender. Arrange in shallow dish with celery. Combine Italian dressing, orange juice, and dill. Pour over vegetables. Chill. To serve, arrange broccoli, orange sections, and sliced egg whites on crisp salad greens.
Prep. time: 30 min. *Serves 4.*

Has the dairy industry brainwashed you into thinking you need to drink milk to obtain calcium? Most animals get their calcium from greens and so should you. Even just 1 cup of steamed broccoli has 100 mg. of calcium—so enjoy!

Broccoli and Bermuda Onion Salad

Per Serving		
Total Fat	0.4	gm
Saturated	0.1	gm
Unsaturated	0.3	gm
Cholesterol	0	mg
Sodium	51	mg
Carbohydrate	10	gm
Protein	3	gm
Fiber	4	gm
Calories	49	

1 c. small broccoli florets

¼ Bermuda (sweet) onion, sliced thin

½ cucumber, thinly sliced

4 T. bottled Italian

dressing (no oil)

2 c. torn romaine lettuce

Chopped pimento

Put first four ingredients in bowl and marinate ½ hour. Add lettuce and toss. Sprinkle pimento on top.
Prep. time: 45 min. *Serves 2.*

Cucumber Salad

Per Serving		
Total Fat	8	gm
Saturated	0.6	gm
Unsaturated	7.4	gm
Cholesterol	0	mg
Sodium	77	mg
Carbohydrate	18	gm
Protein	5	gm
Fiber	5	gm
Calories	139	

½ cucumber, peeled, thinly sliced, and quartered

2 green onions, chopped

1 small tomato, chopped

½ t. oregano

1 T. flax oil

1 t. vegetable broth seasoning

1 c. frozen peas, thawed

2 T. white wine vinegar with tarragon (optional)

Mix all ingredients together and serve on a bed of lettuce.
Prep. time: 20 min. *Serves 2.*

Peas and Mushroom Salad

1 package thawed frozen peas

4 mushrooms, sliced

1 scallion, chopped

¼ c. raw hulled sunflower seeds

¼ red bell pepper, chopped

¼ c. no-oil salad dressing (your favorite)

Per Serving		
Total Fat	5	gm
Saturated	0.5	gm
Unsaturated	4.5	gm
Cholesterol	0	mg
Sodium	96	mg
Carbohydrate	16	gm
Protein	7	gm
Fiber	5	gm
Calories	127	

Toss all ingredients together. Serve cold.
Prep. time: 5 min. after thawing. *Serves 4.*

Vegetables in Mustard Vinaigrette

2 c. broccoli flowerets

3 sliced carrots

¼ c. white wine vinegar

½ t. mustard powder

¼ t. celery seed

Pinch of pepper

¾ c. no-oil herb dressing

¼ lb. sliced raw mushrooms

Per Serving		
Total Fat	1	gm
Saturated	0.1	gm
Unsaturated	0.9	gm
Cholesterol	0	mg
Sodium	65	mg
Carbohydrate	11	gm
Protein	3	gm
Fiber	3	gm
Calories	61	

Steam broccoli and carrots for 5 min. and let cool.
Mix together vinegar, mustard, celery seed, and
pepper. Beat in herb dressing. Place vegetables
in a shallow dish, add mushrooms, and cover with
dressing. Cover dish and chill 3 hours. Remove with
slotted spoon. Serve over lettuce leaves.
Prep. time: 10 min., plus chill time. *Serves 4.*

Chinese Salad

Per Serving

Total Fat	1	gm
Saturated	0.1	gm
Unsaturated	0.9	gm
Cholesterol	0	mg
Sodium	16	mg
Carbohydrate	13	gm
Protein	2	gm
Fiber	2	gm
Calories	60	

¼ lb. mung bean sprouts

½ small Bermuda onion, sliced thin

1 lb. cherry tomatoes, halved

1 small can chopped water chestnuts (or ¼ lb. sliced jicama)

Toss all ingredients together.
Prep. time: 10 min. *Serves 4.*

Rice and Bean Salad

Per Serving

Total Fat	1	gm
Saturated	0.1	gm
Unsaturated	0.9	gm
Cholesterol	0	mg
Sodium	130	mg
Carbohydrate	25	gm
Protein	8	gm
Fiber	3	gm
Calories	135	

½ c. cooked rice

1 c. cooked red kidney or pinto beans, or 1 8-oz. can red kidney or pinto beans

2 hard-boiled egg whites, chopped

½ small onion, chopped fine

1 T. pickle relish

⅛ c. no-oil creamy salad dressing

⅛ t. pepper

⅛ t. celery seed

1 small head Boston lettuce

Mix all ingredients except lettuce and chill for 2 hours.
Serve on lettuce.
Prep. time: 30 min. *Serves 2.*

Carrot Sunshine Salad

2 c. grated raw carrot

1 c. fresh pineapple
  chunks

2 oranges, peeled and cut
  into neat sections

½ c. raisins

1 c. raw sunflower seeds

¼ c. plain nonfat yogurt

Per Serving		
Total Fat	12	gm
Saturated	1.3	gm
Unsaturated	10.7	gm
Cholesterol	0.2	mg
Sodium	17	mg
Carbohydrate	26	gm
Protein	7	gm
Fiber	4	gm
Calories	222	

Mix all ingredients together and chill for several
hours before serving.
Prep. time: 15 min. *Serves 4.*

Cold Lentil Salad

6 c. cooked lentils

¼ c. cilantro, chopped

4 ripe tomatoes, chopped

1 c. No-Oil Salad
Dressing (see page 99)

Per Serving		
Total Fat	1	gm
Saturated	0.1	gm
Unsaturated	0.9	gm
Cholesterol	0	mg
Sodium	43	mg
Carbohydrate	45	gm
Protein	19	gm
Fiber	11	gm
Calories	254	

Combine all ingredients. Let chill in refrigerator at
least 2 hours. Serve on a bed of lettuce as a side dish.
Prep time: 20 min., plus chill time. *Serves 6.*

Greek Salad

Per Serving

Total Fat	1	gm
Saturated	0.4	gm
Unsaturated	0.6	gm
Cholesterol	2	mg
Sodium	100	mg
Carbohydrate	14	gm
Protein	3	gm
Fiber	3	gm
Calories	68	

¼ lb. mixed lettuce

3 cucumbers, skinned and sliced

½ purple onion, sliced thin

3 tomatoes, chopped

1 c. artichoke hearts, packed in water

1 t. ground basil

1 c. No-Oil Salad Dressing (see page 99)

1 T. feta cheese

Mix all ingredients. Let marinate in refrigerator at least 2 hours.
Prep. time: 20 min., plus marinating time. *Serves 6.*

Celery-Spinach Salad

Per Serving

Total Fat	1	gm
Saturated	0.2	gm
Unsaturated	0.8	gm
Cholesterol	0	mg
Sodium	90	mg
Carbohydrate	4	gm
Protein	4	gm
Fiber	2	gm
Calories	32	

1 stalk celery, thinly sliced

½ t. mustard powder

½ t. nutmeg

2 c. torn spinach

1 hard-boiled egg white, sliced

2 oz. mushrooms, sliced

1 ½ T. tarragon vinegar

Toss all ingredients except egg white. Sprinkle sliced egg white over top.
Prep. time: 15 min. *Serves 1.*

Spinach-Mushroom Salad

1 large bunch spinach, stemmed

4 oz. mushrooms, sliced

2 hard-boiled egg whites, chopped

1 small Bermuda onion, chopped

No-oil Italian or herb dressing

Per Serving		
Total Fat	1	gm
Saturated	0	gm
Unsaturated	1	gm
Cholesterol	0	mg
Sodium	129	mg
Carbohydrate	5	gm
Protein	5	gm
Fiber	5	gm
Calories	40	

Combine first 4 ingredients and serve with dressing. Prep. time: 20 min. *Serves 2.*

Sliced Tomato Salad

2 large tomatoes

1 small Bermuda onion

Dash of celery seed

Fresh parsley

No-oil Italian dressing

Per Serving		
Total Fat	0.3	gm
Saturated	0	gm
Unsaturated	0.3	gm
Cholesterol	0	mg
Sodium	8	mg
Carbohydrate	5	gm
Protein	1	gm
Fiber	1	gm
Calories	21	

Slice tomatoes and onions onto individual salad plates. Sprinkle lightly with celery seed; garnish edges with parsley. Serve with Italian dressing. Prep. time: 20 min. *Serves 4.*

Curried Rice Salad

Per Serving

Total Fat	8	gm
Saturated	0.9	gm
Unsaturated	7.1	gm
Cholesterol	0	mg
Sodium	16	mg
Carbohydrate	27	gm
Protein	5	gm
Fiber	3	gm
Calories	196	

½ c. slivered almonds

2 c. cooked brown rice, chilled

¼ t. curry powder

½ c. Tofu Mayonnaise (see page 97)

½ c. celery, finely chopped

1 large bunch spinach, stemmed

Toast almonds by placing them in a dry skillet over medium-high heat and shaking the skillet quickly. Place all ingredients except spinach in a chilled bowl and toss lightly. Serve at once on a bed of spinach. Optional: Substitute lettuce or bean sprouts for spinach.
Prep. time: 30 min. *Serves 2.*

Bean Salad

Per Serving

Total Fat	1	gm
Saturated	0.1	gm
Unsaturated	0.9	gm
Cholesterol	0	mg
Sodium	129	mg
Carbohydrate	21	gm
Protein	5	gm
Fiber	4	gm
Calories	108	

Make a meal out of this by tossing the Bean Salad with lots of romaine lettuce.

1 c. cooked kidney beans

1 c. cooked green beans

1 c. cooked garbanzo beans

1 small Bermuda onion, chopped

½ large green pepper, chopped

½ large red pepper, chopped

½ c. no-oil Italian dressing

3 T. thawed frozen apple juice concentrate

1 t. Salt Sub (see page 235)

1 t. vegetable broth seasoning (see page 128)

Mix first 6 ingredients. Whisk Italian dressing with the last 3 ingredients. Use this to marinate the beans and other vegetables in the refrigerator overnight or all day. Prep. time: 45 min., plus marinating time. *Serves 6.*

No-Cook Bean Salad

1 16-oz. can wax beans, rinsed

1 16-oz. can garbanzo beans, rinsed

1 16-oz. can kidney beans, rinsed

½ c. chopped green pepper

½ c. chopped onion (yellow, red, or green)

4 T. cider vinegar

1 T. flax oil

1 T. vegetable broth seasoning

⅛ t. black pepper

Per Serving

Total Fat	6	gm
Saturated	0.5	gm
Unsaturated	5.5	gm
Cholesterol	0	mg
Sodium	458	mg
Carbohydrate	45	gm
Protein	14	gm
Fiber	14	gm
Calories	275	

Combine all ingredients in a bowl with a tight-sealing lid (such as Tupperware®). Allow to marinate for at least an hour, gently shaking the bowl several times to mix the seasonings with the vegetables. Prep. time: 20 min. *Serves 4.*

Triple Bean Salad

1 c. cooked green beans

1 c. cooked wax beans, or garbanzo beans

1 c. cooked red kidney beans

2 T. chopped green onions

¾ c. Italian dressing (no salt, no oil)

Dash of fresh ground pepper

Lettuce leaves

Per Serving

Total Fat	1	gm
Saturated	0.1	gm
Unsaturated	0.9	gm
Cholesterol	0	mg
Sodium	496	mg
Carbohydrate	30	gm
Protein	9	gm
Fiber	10	gm
Calories	148	

Mix first 3 ingredients. Add green onions and Italian dressing. Toss to mix. Refrigerate several hours. Before serving, toss again, then drain. Dash with fresh ground pepper. Serve on lettuce leaves. Prep. time: 20 min. *Serves 6.*

Basic Green Salad

Per Serving

Total Fat	5	gm
Saturated	0.5	gm
Unsaturated	4.5	gm
Cholesterol	0	mg
Sodium	47	mg
Carbohydrate	13	gm
Protein	6	gm
Fiber	4	gm
Calories	110	

1 head romaine, butterleaf, redleaf, or greenleaf lettuce

1 carrot, grated

1 wedge cabbage, shredded

1 large tomato, sliced

¼ c. raw hulled sunflower seeds

2 oz. alfalfa sprouts

5 oz. thawed frozen peas

Wash lettuce and dry thoroughly. Tear lettuce into a 6-quart bowl. Add remaining ingredients. Toss well with your favorite dressing from the recipes beginning on page 97, or use a store-bought, no-oil dressing.
Prep. time: 25 min. *Serves 2.*

Large Green Salad with Garbanzo Beans

Per Serving

Total Fat	6	gm
Saturated	0.5	gm
Unsaturated	5.5	gm
Cholesterol	0	mg
Sodium	322	mg
Carbohydrate	29	gm
Protein	9	gm
Fiber	9	gm
Calories	187	

1 head Boston lettuce

1 tomato, chopped

1 c. canned julienne beets

¼ c. chopped green onions

½ c. canned kidney beans, rinsed

½ c. canned garbanzo beans, rinsed

2 t. flax oil

2 T. cider vinegar

1 T. vegetable broth seasoning

Wash lettuce and dry thoroughly. Tear lettuce into bite-sized pieces. Toss with remaining ingredients. Serve on a dinner plate.
Prep. time: 20 min. *Serves 2.*

Green Salad Romana

6 outer leaves from head of romaine lettuce (save inner leaves for a hearts of romaine salad)

¼ c. chopped green onions

1 small tomato, chopped

1 T. flax oil

1 t. vegetable broth seasoning

1 T. cider vinegar

1 T. water

Per Serving		
Total Fat	7	gm
Saturated	0.5	gm
Unsaturated	6.5	gm
Cholesterol	0	mg
Sodium	8	mg
Carbohydrate	4	gm
Protein	1	gm
Fiber	1	gm
Calories	79	

Tear the lettuce leaves into bite-size pieces. Toss with the remaining ingredients.
Prep. time: 20 min. *Serves 2.*

Chef Salad

We use thin strips of cooked white meat turkey or chicken on top of this. It's impressive, colorful, healthy, and delicious for family and friends.

1 small head leafy green lettuce

1 c. canned garbanzo beans, rinsed

½ c. canned kidney beans, rinsed

½ c. frozen peas, rinsed to thaw

2 T. chopped green onion

1 T. hulled sunflower seeds

1 c. unsweetened julienne beets

1 large tomato, cut in chunks

6 asparagus spears

Per Serving		
Total Fat	5	gm
Saturated	0.5	gm
Unsaturated	4.5	gm
Cholesterol	0	mg
Sodium	447	mg
Carbohydrate	51	gm
Protein	16	gm
Fiber	14	gm
Calories	243	

Place large serving plates in freezer to chill. Wash lettuce, let drain, and tear into bite-size pieces. Combine all ingredients except asparagus spears (reserve for garnish). Toss with Honey-Lemon Dressing (see page 98). Divide into two portions, heaping each onto a large chilled plate. Lay the asparagus spears over the top.
Prep. time: 25 min. *Serves 2.*

Potato Salad

Per Serving

Total Fat	1	gm
Saturated	0.1	gm
Unsaturated	0.9	gm
Cholesterol	1	mg
Sodium	164	mg
Carbohydrate	61	gm
Protein	14	gm
Fiber	5	gm
Calories	306	

2 c. cooked, cubed potatoes

1 small onion, chopped

½ c. chopped celery

3 hard-boiled egg whites, chopped

1 t. Salt Sub (see page 235)

1 T. vinegar

1 t. mustard powder

½ c. plain nonfat yogurt

Combine all ingredients well. To blend flavors, refrigerate a few hours before serving.
Prep. time: 35 min., plus refrigeration time. *Serves 2.*

Red Potato Salad

Per Serving

Total Fat	1	gm
Saturated	0.2	gm
Unsaturated	0.8	gm
Cholesterol	0	mg
Sodium	155	mg
Carbohydrate	104	gm
Protein	10	gm
Fiber	12	gm
Calories	446	

6 red potatoes, cooked and cut into large chunks

2 stalks celery, chopped

1 tomato, chopped

½ red onion, chopped

½ c. No-Oil Salad Dressing (see page 99)

Mix and refrigerate a few hours before serving.
Prep. time: 25 min., plus refrigeration time. *Serves 2.*

Tuna-Pasta Salad

If you've got children who like the tuna and pasta, but don't like the Italian dressing, try replacing it with Tofu Mayonnaise (see page 97).

1 small can all-white tuna in water (6.5 oz.)

1 tomato, chopped

1 bell pepper, chopped

½ c. celery, chopped

1 apple, chopped

1 c. cooked pasta shells

4 T. Italian or herb dressing (see page 99)

Red leaf lettuce

2 lemon wedges, optional

Per Serving		
Total Fat	3	gm
Saturated	0.4	gm
Unsaturated	2.6	gm
Cholesterol	17	mg
Sodium	143	mg
Carbohydrate	41	gm
Protein	28	gm
Fiber	6	gm
Calories	284	

Mix all ingredients with Italian Dressing. Serve on a bed of red leaf lettuce. Garnish with lemon wedges, if desired.
Prep. time: 15 min. *Serves 2.*

Macaroni Salad

1 c. uncooked salad macaroni (whole wheat if you wish)

1 T. olive oil

2 hard-boiled egg whites, chopped

1 T. minced green onion

2 T. minced sweet or dill pickle (whichever you prefer)

1 c. cooked peas

4 T. chopped pimento

2 T. cider vinegar

1 t. prepared mustard

2 t. vegetable broth seasoning

Red leaf lettuce

½ apple, sliced, optional

Per Serving		
Total Fat	8	gm
Saturated	1.1	gm
Unsaturated	6.9	gm
Cholesterol	0	mg
Sodium	171	mg
Carbohydrate	55	gm
Protein	15	gm
Fiber	4	gm
Calories	349	

Cook the macaroni according to the package directions. When the macaroni is cooked, drain and rinse, and immediately toss with the olive oil. Add the remaining ingredients in the order given, tossing with vinegar, mustard, and vegetable broth seasoning. Serve on a bed of lettuce. Garnish with apple slices, if desired.
Prep. time: 25 min. *Serves 2.*

Pineapple Fruit Salad Dressing

2 c. plain nonfat yogurt
½ c. drained
    unsweetened pineapple
½ c. unsweetened
    pineapple juice

Blend all ingredients until smooth.
Prep. time: 10 min. Serving size is 2 T. *Makes 3 cups.*

Spring Fruit Salad Dressing

2 c. plain nonfat yogurt
½ c. any unsweetened
    fruit chopped
    (strawberries, peaches,
    nectarines, etc.)
½ c. any unsweetened
    fruit juice (orange,
    pineapple, apple, etc.)

Stir all ingredients with a fork until well mixed.
Prep. time: 10 min. Serving size is 2 T. *Makes 3 cups.*

Tangy Fruit Salad Dressing

2 c. plain nonfat yogurt

1 c. thawed frozen
orange juice
concentrate

1 c. raisins

4 apples, peeled, cored,
and chopped

Per Serving		
Total Fat	0.1	gm
Saturated	0	gm
Unsaturated	0.1	gm
Cholesterol	0	mg
Sodium	7	mg
Carbohydrate	7	gm
Protein	0.8	gm
Fiber	0.5	gm
Calories	30	

Stir all ingredients with a fork until well mixed.
Prep. time: 15 min. Serving size is 2 T. *Makes 6 cups.*

Tofu Mayonnaise

1 lb. washed, drained
tofu

¼ c. granular lecithin

¼ c. lemon juice or apple
cider vinegar

½ t. Salt Sub
(see page 235)

1 T. honey

¾ c. flax oil

½ t. garlic powder,
dill weed, or tarragon,
optional

Per Serving		
Total Fat	16	gm
Saturated	1.9	gm
Unsaturated	14.1	gm
Cholesterol	0	mg
Sodium	6	mg
Carbohydrate	3	gm
Protein	5	gm
Fiber	0.4	gm
Calories	171	

Cut tofu into large chunks and place in blender. Add
all remaining ingredients, except ½ c. of the oil, and
blend. With blender at medium-high speed, slowly,
drop by drop, add remaining oil. Add ½ t. of garlic
powder, dill weed, or tarragon, if desired. Blend
several minutes until very smooth and thick. Chill.
Prep. time: 20 min. Serving size is 2 T. *Makes 2 cups.*

Honey-Lemon Dressing

Per Serving

Total Fat	10	gm
Saturated	1.4	gm
Unsaturated	8.6	gm
Cholesterol	0	mg
Sodium	1	mg
Carbohydrate	5	gm
Protein	1	gm
Fiber	0	gm
Calories	109	

Use a crude, expeller-pressed sesame oil that won't overpower the honey and lemon.

3 T. lemon juice

1 T. honey

1 T. vegetable broth seasoning

2 T. water

3 T. crude, expeller-pressed sesame oil

Blend or shake together.
Prep. time: 5 min. Serving size is 2 T. *Makes ½ cup.*

Buttermilk-Celery Seed Dressing

Per Serving

Total Fat	0.3	gm
Saturated	0.2	gm
Unsaturated	0.1	gm
Cholesterol	1	mg
Sodium	32	mg
Carbohydrate	2	gm
Protein	1	gm
Fiber	0	gm
Calories	16	

1 c. buttermilk

1 t. lemon juice

1 t. honey

½ t. celery seed

Combine ingredients and beat well. Refrigerate until ready to use.
Prep. time: 8 min. Serving size is 2 T. *Makes 1 cup.*

Italian Dressing

Substituting fresh garlic instead of the garlic powder is a good way to get all of garlic's healthful properties into your dressing.

¼ c. lemon juice

¼ c. vinegar

¼ c. unsweetened apple juice

½ t. oregano

½ t. mustard powder

½ t. garlic powder

½ t. paprika

½ t. thyme

¼ t. rosemary

Per Serving		
Total Fat	0.2	gm
Saturated	0	gm
Unsaturated	0.2	gm
Cholesterol	0	mg
Sodium	3	mg
Carbohydrate	3	gm
Protein	0.2	gm
Fiber	0.1	gm
Calories	11	

Blend all ingredients in a blender. Chill well before serving.
Prep. time: 10 min. Serving size is 2 T. *Makes ¾ cup.*

No-Oil Salad Dressing

2 oz. wine vinegar

4 oz. water

½ t. frozen apple juice concentrate

¼ t. oregano

⅛ t. pepper

Per Serving		
Total Fat	0	gm
Saturated	0	gm
Unsaturated	0	gm
Cholesterol	0	mg
Sodium	1	mg
Carbohydrate	2	gm
Protein	0	gm
Fiber	0	gm
Calories	2	

Combine all ingredients. Refrigerate until ready to use. Mix vigorously before pouring.
Prep. time: 5 min. Serving size is 2 T. *Makes ⅓ cup.*

Cucumber-Dill Salad Dressing

Per Serving	
Total Fat	0 gm
Saturated	0 gm
Unsaturated	0 gm
Cholesterol	0.2 mg
Sodium	6 mg
Carbohydrate	2 gm
Protein	1 gm
Fiber	0.2 gm
Calories	9

1 ¼ c. peeled, seeded, and sliced cucumber

¼ c. plain nonfat yogurt

2 T. fresh lemon juice

1 t. dried dill weed

½ t. sugar

¼ t. onion powder

¼ t. garlic powder

⅛ t. pepper

Combine all ingredients in an electric blender or food processor. Cover and blend until cucumber is puréed. Serve over salad greens, sliced vegetables, or fish. Prep. time: 15 min. Serving size is 2 T. *Makes 1 cup.*

Salt-Free Flax Oil Italian Dressing

Per Serving	
Total Fat	14 gm
Saturated	1 gm
Unsaturated	13 gm
Cholesterol	0 mg
Sodium	0.4 mg
Carbohydrate	1 gm
Protein	0.2 gm
Fiber	0 gm
Calories	125

Be sure to use a crude, expeller-pressed oil at all times. If you use a "bad" oil with this dressing, you'll cancel out all the good benefits of not using salt.

½ c. flax oil

¼ c. vinegar

¼ c. water

1 clove garlic, minced

¼ t. cayenne pepper

¼ t. dry mustard

¼ t. oregano

1 t. frozen apple juice concentrate

Combine all ingredients in a salad dressing bottle. Shake well. Store in refrigerator until ready to serve. Prep. time: 5 min. Serving size is 2 T. *Makes 1 cup.*

Tomato Juice Salad Dressing

1 c. low-sodium tomato juice

¼ c. fresh lemon juice

2 T. finely grated celery

1 clove garlic, finely minced

½ t. dried oregano

¼ t. pepper

Per Serving		
Total Fat	0	gm
Saturated	0	gm
Unsaturated	0	gm
Cholesterol	0	mg
Sodium	4	mg
Carbohydrate	3	gm
Protein	0.3	gm
Fiber	0.4	gm
Calories	10	

Combine all ingredients in jar. Shake vigorously and refrigerate several hours before using.
Prep. time: 10 min. Serving size is 2 T.
Makes 1 ⅓ cups.

Traditional French Dressing

1 c. low-sodium tomato juice

2 T. rice vinegar

1 t. onion flakes

⅛ t. sweet basil

⅛ t. mustard powder

⅛ t. garlic powder

⅛ t. pepper

Per Serving		
Total Fat	0.1	gm
Saturated	0	gm
Unsaturated	0.1	gm
Cholesterol	0	mg
Sodium	3	mg
Carbohydrate	2	gm
Protein	0.4	gm
Fiber	0.4	gm
Calories	8	

Mix all ingredients well and chill before serving.
Prep. time: 5 min. Serving size is 2 T. *Makes 1 cup.*

Zesty French Dressing

1 T. arrowroot
2 T. cold water
2 c. rice vinegar, or any other mild vinegar
2 c. V-8® vegetable juice, unsalted
1 c. tomato juice
⅓ c. lemon juice
3 T. thawed apple juice concentrate

3 T. low-sodium tomato paste
1 small onion, chopped
½ green pepper, chopped
1 t. celery seed
1 t. dill seed
1 t. paprika
⅛ t. cayenne pepper
1 t. finely minced parsley

Mix arrowroot with cold water to make a paste. Combine remaining ingredients except parsley in a saucepan. Heat to boiling, then gradually add arrowroot paste. Cook for 5 more min., stirring as needed. Cool and transfer to blender and blend. Add parsley and stir. Chill well before serving.
Prep. time: 25 min. Serving size is 2 T. *Makes 6 cups.*

Tangy French Dressing

2 c. rice vinegar or any other mild vinegar
2 c. V-8® vegetable juice, unsalted
1 c. tomato sauce
1/3 c. lemon juice
3 T. apple juice concentrate
3 T. tomato paste
1 onion

½ green pepper, chopped
1 t. celery seed
1 t. dill weed
1 t. paprika
⅛ t. cayenne pepper
1 T. arrowroot mixed with 2 T. water to make paste
1 t. finely minced parsley

Combine all ingredients in a saucepan, except for the arrowroot paste and minced parsley. Heat to boiling; mix in arrowroot paste. Cook 5 min., stirring occasionally. Cool and transfer to a blender; blend well. Add parsley, and stir. Chill before serving. Store in refrigerator.
Prep. time: 25 min. Serving size is 2 T. *Makes 6 cups.*

Green Chili Pepper Dressing

½ c. low sodium tomato juice

1 can (8 oz.) tomato juice

1 c. plain nonfat yogurt

1 t. lemon juice

1 t. green chilis, diced

1 t. honey

½ t. dill weed

½ t. fresh parsley

Per Serving		
Total Fat	0	gm
Saturated	0	gm
Unsaturated	0	gm
Cholesterol	0.3	mg
Sodium	13	mg
Carbohydrate	3	gm
Protein	1	gm
Fiber	0.1	gm
Calories	15	

Blend all ingredients in a blender until smooth.
Prep. time: 15 min. Serving size is 2 T.
Makes 2 cups.

Garden Fresh Dressing

4 ripe, red tomatoes

2 young green onions

4 T. fresh parsley, chopped

¼ c. lemon juice

1 garlic clove

1 t. basil, ground

Per Serving		
Total Fat	0.3	gm
Saturated	0	gm
Unsaturated	0.3	gm
Cholesterol	0	mg
Sodium	9	mg
Carbohydrate	5	gm
Protein	1	gm
Fiber	1	gm
Calories	22	

Blend all ingredients in a blender until smooth.
Prep. time: 15 min. Serving size is 2 T. *Makes ¾ cup.*

Beans, Rice, & Grains

Baked Beans

Per Serving

Total Fat	2	gm
Saturated	0.3	gm
Unsaturated	1.7	gm
Cholesterol	0	mg
Sodium	57	mg
Carbohydrate	32	gm
Protein	8	gm
Fiber	8	gm
Calories	177	

These beans make such great leftovers, you might want to double or triple the recipe. "Unsulphured" blackstrap molasses is easy to find in your grocery or health food store. Unsulphured simply means no sulphur was used during processing.

¾ c. celery, chopped small (pea size)

2 c. cooked pinto beans

⅓ c. unsalted spaghetti sauce

¼ c. water

¾ c. chopped onion

1 T. natural catsup (made with honey)

1 T. unsulphured blackstrap molasses

2 t. vegetable broth seasoning

Preheat oven to 350° F. Mix all ingredients in a 2-quart casserole dish and cover. Bake for 45 min. Prep. time: 1 hour. *Serves 4.*

Baked Lima Beans

Per Serving

Total Fat	1	gm
Saturated	0.1	gm
Unsaturated	0.9	gm
Cholesterol	0	mg
Sodium	37	mg
Carbohydrate	28	gm
Protein	6	gm
Fiber	8	gm
Calories	134	

2 c. dried lima beans

2 onions, thinly sliced

2 carrots, scraped, finely diced

1 c. chopped tomatoes

1 clove garlic, finely minced

1 c. unsalted tomato juice

½ t. Worcestershire sauce

⅛ t. pepper

Preheat oven to 350° F. Soak lima beans for several hours or overnight. Discard soaking water. Place lima beans in a non-stick baking dish. Add onions, carrots, tomatoes, and garlic. Separately, combine tomato juice, Worcestershire sauce, and pepper; pour over bean mixture. Mix well. Cover tightly with a lid or foil. Bake 2 hours, or until beans are tender. Prep. time: 2 hours and 30 min., plus soaking time. *Serves 6.*

Lima-Corn Casserole

Use dried or frozen lima beans instead of canned ones, which are loaded with salt.

1 c. dried lima beans (can substitute 2 c. frozen lima beans)

2 c. cooked corn kernels

2 onions, thinly sliced

1 can (28 oz.) tomatoes

½ t. paprika

¼ t. dry mustard

¼ t. dried rosemary

¼ c. whole wheat bread crumbs

Per Serving		
Total Fat	3	gm
Saturated	0.4	gm
Unsaturated	2.6	gm
Cholesterol	0	mg
Sodium	48	mg
Carbohydrate	59	gm
Protein	9	gm
Fiber	10	gm
Calories	292	

Soak lima beans overnight in cold water. Preheat oven to 350° F. Cook lima beans over low heat 2 hours, or until beans are soft. Combine cooked lima beans with cooked corn in a 2-quart, non-stick baking dish. Combine onions, tomatoes, paprika, mustard, and rosemary; spoon over top of beans and corn. Top with bread crumbs. Bake for 30 min.
Prep. time: 2 hours and 45 min., plus soaking time.
Serves 6.

Chili

For a treat, brown some white turkey or chicken meat and use it instead of the barley. Serve the chili with corn bread.

1 medium yellow onion, chopped

3 c. cooked pinto beans with liquid

1 c. cooked barley

¾ c. unsalted spaghetti sauce

2 T. vegetable broth seasoning

3 T. chile salsa

Per Serving		
Total Fat	3	gm
Saturated	0.5	gm
Unsaturated	2.5	gm
Cholesterol	0	mg
Sodium	172	mg
Carbohydrate	54	gm
Protein	13	gm
Fiber	14	gm
Calories	293	

In a pan-sprayed non-stick skillet sauté the onion. Place sautéed onion, 1 ½ c. pinto beans, and liquids in blender; blend coarsely. Pour the blended mixture into a pot with the remaining ingredients and simmer until the flavors are thoroughly blended, about 10 min.
Prep. time: 30 min. *Serves 4.*

Spicy Chili

Per Serving

Total Fat	2	gm
Saturated	0.2	gm
Unsaturated	1.8	gm
Cholesterol	0	mg
Sodium	45	mg
Carbohydrate	56	gm
Protein	18	gm
Fiber	7	gm
Calories	298	

1 lb. kidney and/or pinto beans

1 onion, finely chopped

1 stalk celery, finely chopped

3 cloves minced garlic

1 ½ t. paprika

1 ½ T. chili powder

½ t. cumin

1 t. oregano

2 c. peeled fresh or canned tomatoes

4 T. tomato paste

⅛ t. Tabasco® pepper sauce

2 T. low-sodium soy sauce or vegetable broth seasoning

3 c. cooked brown rice (optional)

Cook kidney and/or pinto beans, reserving ¾ c. of the liquid. Simmer beans with liquid and remaining ingredients in a large pot for about 1 hour. (Keep an eye on the pot for spillovers or scorching. Add more liquid if necessary.) Serve over a scoop of brown rice, if desired.

Prep. time: 1 hour and 30 min. Makes 1 ½ quarts. *Serves 6.*

Red Beans

Per Serving

Total Fat	1	gm
Saturated	0.1	gm
Unsaturated	0.9	gm
Cholesterol	0	mg
Sodium	3	mg
Carbohydrate	31	gm
Protein	12	gm
Fiber	7	gm
Calories	171	

3 c. red beans (cooked)

2 cloves garlic, peeled, minced

Combine ingredients, then purée in a blender or food processor.

Prep. time: 5 min. *Serves 4.*

Creole Lentils

Filé powder is made from the pulverized leaves of sassafras and it's used as a thickener in soups and gumbos. If you can't fit it in your grocery store's spice aisle, look for something called "gumbo mixture," and use that.

½ c. dried lentils

1 green pepper, seeded, finely chopped

1 onion, finely chopped

2 tomatoes, finely chopped

⅛ t. pepper

⅛ t. thyme

1 T. olive oil

⅛ t. filé powder, optional

2 c. cooked brown rice

Per Serving		
Total Fat	5	gm
Saturated	0.7	gm
Unsaturated	4.3	gm
Cholesterol	0	mg
Sodium	107	mg
Carbohydrate	41	gm
Protein	8	gm
Fiber	5	gm
Calories	230	

Cover lentils with water and soak overnight. Drain, cover with fresh water, and cook over low heat, covered, until lentils are tender, about 1 hour. In a non-stick skillet coated with a nonfat cooking spray, sauté green pepper and onion until limp. Add tomatoes, pepper, thyme, and olive oil. Add filé powder, if desired. Cook 5 min. Drain lentils and add to tomatoes; simmer, covered, 5 min. more. Serve over cooked brown rice.

Prep. time: 1 hour and 30 min. *Serves 4.*

The term "Creole" is loosely used to indicate descendants of French or Spanish settlers. Creole comes from the Spanish word "Criollo," and means, "native to the place."

Lentil Stew

Try adding fresh tomatoes, zucchini, green peppers, ripe corn, and rice to your Lentil Stew for richness. Experiment! With soups and stews, the more vegetables you add—the better they taste. Leftovers Suggestion: Toast a corn tortilla in a toaster and use warmed, leftover lentil stew as a bean filling: place 2 T. in center of tortilla with 1 t. or more of mild chile salsa. Roll and eat.

4 c. water

1 c. uncooked lentils

1 medium potato, scrubbed, cut into bite-size pieces

1 large carrot, cut into bite-size pieces

1 T. tomato sauce

1 T. vegetable broth seasoning

Bring the water to a boil and add the lentils. Turn down the heat and simmer for 15 min. Add the potato and carrot; cook for 30 min. more. Add the remaining ingredients, and cook a final 10 to 15 min. Serve with bread or muffins and a salad.
Prep. time: 1 hour and 10 min. *Serves 4.*

Brown Rice

1 c. brown rice

2 ½ c. water

Preheat oven to 400° F. Place rice in a baking dish that has a tight-fitting lid. Cover with water. Place in oven and cook covered for 1 hour. The rice will absorb all the water and cook to perfection. If you like your rice seasoned, add a dash of basil, saffron, garlic, onions, or pepper, separately or in combination, before cooking. Also, you can use a rice cooker instead of this baking method, if you prefer.
Prep. time: 1 hour. *Serves 5.*

Orange Rice

1 c. brown rice

1 c. orange juice

1 ½ c. water

½ t. dried dill weed

¼ c. sliced scallions

Per Serving		
Total Fat	1	gm
Saturated	0.2	gm
Unsaturated	0.8	gm
Cholesterol	0	mg
Sodium	4	mg
Carbohydrate	29	gm
Protein	3	gm
Fiber	1	gm
Calories	136	

Combine rice, orange juice, water, and dill weed in a large saucepan. Add scallions. Bring to a boil, turn heat low and cover tightly. Simmer over low heat for 40 min., stirring once during cooking time. Add additional water, if needed.
Prep. time: 50 min. *Serves 6.*

Brown Rice Español

1 c. short grain brown rice

2 ½ c. water

1 c. chopped tomatoes

1 green pepper, finely diced

1 onion, finely diced

2 T. chopped fresh parsley

⅛ t. pepper

Per Serving		
Total Fat	1	gm
Saturated	0.2	gm
Unsaturated	0.8	gm
Cholesterol	0	mg
Sodium	10	mg
Carbohydrate	30	gm
Protein	3	gm
Fiber	2	gm
Calories	143	

Place rice and water in a saucepan; bring to a boil. Stir. Cover and cook for 40 min., fluffing once with a fork. When done, rice should be tender and water should be evaporated. In a separate saucepan, cook tomatoes, green pepper, onion, parsley, and pepper. Toss tomato mixture through cooked rice and serve.
Prep. time: 45 min. *Serves 6.*

Mock Meatballs

Per Serving

Total Fat	7	gm
Saturated	0.6	gm
Unsaturated	6.4	gm
Cholesterol	0	mg
Sodium	71	mg
Carbohydrate	20	gm
Protein	6	gm
Fiber	3	gm
Calories	161	

1 c. cooked lentils
1 c. cooked brown rice
2 egg whites, beaten
½ c. whole wheat bread crumbs
½ c. finely chopped pecans
½ medium onion, finely chopped
1 clove garlic, minced
¼ t. oregano
1 t. soy sauce
⅛ c. chopped parsley

Preheat oven to 400° F. Combine lentils and rice with beaten egg whites. Add remaining ingredients and form into balls. Place mock meatballs on a non-stick cookie sheet coated with nonfat cooking spray. Cook for 20 min. Serve with spaghetti. Note: Do not leave mock meatballs in the oven unless covered completely, or they'll dry out. Also, do not soak mock meatballs in sauce, or they'll disintegrate. They may, however, be served with sauce over them.
Prep. time: 45 min. *Serves 6.*

Rice Raffaele

Per Serving

Total Fat	5	gm
Saturated	0.8	gm
Unsaturated	4.2	gm
Cholesterol	0	mg
Sodium	90	mg
Carbohydrate	49	gm
Protein	7	gm
Fiber	8	gm
Calories	261	

This recipe came from an Italian gentleman who came to the Institute years ago.

½ small onion, chopped
8 oz. fresh mushrooms, chopped
1 large green pepper, chopped
4 small zucchini, sliced and quartered
2 T. tomato paste
1 c. water
1 T. olive oil
2 T. mild chile salsa
½ t. oregano
2 T. vegetable broth seasoning
3 c. cooked brown rice

In a non-stick skillet coated with nonfat cooking spray, sauté onion, mushrooms, green pepper, and zucchini. Add tomato paste and water; stir. Add remaining ingredients, except rice, and simmer for 15 min. Stir in rice and heat through for 5 more min.
Prep. time: 45 min. *Serves 4.*

Green Rice Casserole

If you can't find hoop cheese, try using farmer cheese or go ahead and separate the curds in cottage cheese and rinse off all the cream.

1 clove garlic, minced

½ c. chopped onion

½ c. chopped celery

¼ c. walnuts

1 T. olive oil

½ c. chopped parsley

1 c. nonfat cottage cheese

4 egg whites, beaten frothy

1 t. Salt Sub (see page 235)

2 c. nonfat milk

2 c. cooked brown rice

Per Serving		
Total Fat	23	gm
Saturated	1	gm
Unsaturated	22	gm
Cholesterol	55	mg
Sodium	395	mg
Carbohydrate	43	gm
Protein	34	gm
Fiber	5	gm
Calories	573	

Preheat oven to 350° F. Coat a non-stick skillet with nonfat cooking spray. Heat skillet and sauté garlic, onion, and celery. When almost tender, add walnuts. Stir quickly, about 1 min. Remove from heat. In a bowl, mix remaining ingredients. Add sautéed vegetables. Pour into a pan-sprayed, non-stick baking dish. Bake for 30 to 40 min., or until firm.
Prep. time: 1 hour. *Serves 4.*

Millet and Brussels Sprouts Amandine

Per Serving		
Total Fat	10	gm
Saturated	1	gm
Unsaturated	9	gm
Cholesterol	0	mg
Sodium	25	mg
Carbohydrate	64	gm
Protein	15	gm
Fiber	13	gm
Calories	399	

4 T. vegetable broth seasoning

4 c. water

1 ½ c. millet

¼ c. chopped almonds

1 tomato, peeled and chopped

8 precooked brussels sprouts, chopped

1 t. almond extract

Stir vegetable broth seasoning into water. Cook millet in the seasoned water for 30 to 40 min. Add almonds, tomato, Brussels sprouts, and almond extract. Simmer 15 min. more. Be careful to watch for burning. If necessary, add more liquid. Top with a small amount of liquid Butter Buds, if desired. Prep. time: 60 min. *Serves 4.*

Baked Rice and Peas Amandine

Per Serving		
Total Fat	2	gm
Saturated	0.3	gm
Unsaturated	1.7	gm
Cholesterol	0	mg
Sodium	29	mg
Carbohydrate	24	gm
Protein	4	gm
Fiber	2	gm
Calories	133	

This is a favorite side dish in the Whitaker household, where it's used as a side dish for a turkey breast dinner. Try adding some bread crumbs to the recipe before baking it and use it to stuff the turkey instead of as a side dish. It's great.

1 c. chopped onions

1 c. chopped celery

½ c. sliced mushrooms

2 ½ c. Salt-Free Chicken Broth (see page 202)

1 c. brown rice

¾ t. poultry seasoning

1 c. green peas, fresh or frozen

2 T. slivered almonds

Preheat oven to 350° F. In a non-stick skillet, simmer onions, celery, and mushrooms in ½ c. chicken broth, until vegetables are tender. Pour into a 2-quart, non-stick baking dish. Add rice, remaining broth, poultry seasoning, and peas. Cover; bake for 40 min., or until rice is tender and liquid is absorbed. Fluff with a fork. Spoon into serving dish; sprinkle with almonds. Prep. time: 60 min. *Serves 8.*

Mexican Barley Supper

1 zucchini, sliced and
   quartered
4 oz. fresh mushrooms,
   sliced
½ c. water
4 T. salsa (or however
   much you prefer)

1 c. cooked barley
1 T. hulled sunflower
   seeds
1 T. vegetable broth
   seasoning
4 slices whole wheat
   toast

Per Serving		
Total Fat	6	gm
Saturated	1	gm
Unsaturated	5	gm
Cholesterol	0.4	mg
Sodium	295	mg
Carbohydrate	28	gm
Protein	5	gm
Fiber	7	gm
Calories	176	

In a non-stick skillet coated with nonfat cooking
spray, sauté zucchini and mushrooms. Add water and
salsa; cook 3 min. Add barley, sunflower seeds, and
vegetable broth seasoning. Serve over toast.
Prep. time: 25 min. *Serves 4.*

Tabouli

*This is a very satisfying meal all by itself. Look for
bulgur wheat in the ethnic section of your grocery
store.*

3 c. water
1 ¼ c. uncooked bulgur
3 chopped scallions
1 c. minced fresh parsley
3 tomatoes, peeled and
   finely chopped
Juice of two lemons

¼ c. flax oil
Salt Sub (see page 235)
   to taste
Crisp chilled lettuce
Tomato wedges
1 slice Bermuda onion

Per Serving		
Total Fat	30	gm
Saturated	2.9	gm
Unsaturated	27.1	gm
Cholesterol	0	mg
Sodium	48	mg
Carbohydrate	84	gm
Protein	14	gm
Fiber	25	gm
Calories	616	

Bring water to a boil and pour over bulgur. Let it
stand for 1 hour or until grain is light and fluffy.
Press out excess water through a colander. Place in a
bowl and mix with scallions, parsley, chopped
tomatoes, lemon juice, flax oil, and Salt Sub. Chill
several hours before serving. Serve on a bed of crisp
chilled lettuce and garnish with tomato wedges and
an onion slice.
Prep. time: 1 hour and 30 min. *Serves 2.*

Wheat Pilaf

Per Serving

Total Fat	3	gm
Saturated	0.5	gm
Unsaturated	2.5	gm
Cholesterol	0	mg
Sodium	104	mg
Carbohydrate	50	gm
Protein	8	gm
Fiber	12	gm
Calories	279	

½ c. finely chopped onion
1 c. bulgur
2 T. liquid Butter Buds
2 T. vegetable broth seasoning
2 c. water
¼ c. fresh orange juice

1 T. cooking sherry
½ c. dried figs, finely chopped
2 T. sesame seeds
1 t. finely grated orange peel

In a non-stick skillet coated with nonfat cooking spray, sauté onion until soft. Stir in bulgur, then add Butter Buds and vegetable broth seasoning mixed with 2 c. water. Add orange juice and sherry. Cover; simmer over low heat for ½ hour. Stir in figs, sesame seeds, and orange peel. Cover again; continue to cook for 10 min.
Serve hot. Prep. time: 1 hour and 30 min. *Serves 4.*

Curried Lentils

Per Serving

Total Fat	1	gm
Saturated	0.1	gm
Unsaturated	0.9	gm
Cholesterol	0	mg
Sodium	329	mg
Carbohydrate	50	gm
Protein	19	gm
Fiber	12	gm
Calories	272	

2 c. cooked lentils
1 small can crushed tomatoes
2 cloves garlic, peeled, minced

1 t. chopped cilantro
1 t. curry powder

Combine all ingredients. Chill for 1 hour.
Prep. time: 10 min., plus chill time. *Serves 4.*

Rice Dinner Vegetariana

1 c. brown rice (long, medium, or short grain)

1 c. sliced carrots

2 c. lima beans

1 c. peas

½ c. sliced mushrooms

½ c. cauliflower florets

1 c. fresh broccoli pieces

2 t. Salt Sub (see page 235)

1 t. curry powder

Per Serving		
Total Fat	2	gm
Saturated	0.4	gm
Unsaturated	1.6	gm
Cholesterol	0	mg
Sodium	100	mg
Carbohydrate	63	gm
Protein	12	gm
Fiber	9	gm
Calories	313	

Cook rice according to package directions. Steam vegetables in another pan. Add to rice. Add Salt Sub and curry powder. Mix well. Serve immediately. Variation: Substitute barley for rice. Prep. time: 50 min. *Serves 4.*

Pasta

Spaghetti with Marinara Sauce

Per Serving

Total Fat	8	gm
Saturated	1.1	gm
Unsaturated	6.9	gm
Cholesterol	0	mg
Sodium	30	mg
Carbohydrate	61	gm
Protein	9	gm
Fiber	1	gm
Calories	346	

4 oz. uncooked pasta

¼ c. chopped onions

¼ c. minced carrot

1 large clove garlic, minced

⅛ t. black pepper

1 can (15 oz.) peeled Italian tomatoes, diced

1 small bay leaf, crushed

⅛ t. dried thyme

1 T. olive oil

4 oz. low-fat fish (red snapper, halibut, etc.), broiled or steamed, optional

1 T. honey

½ t. grated lemon rind

Vegetable broth seasoning, optional

1 T. minced fresh parsley

Cook pasta according to label directions while making the sauce. Drain pasta just before adding the sauce to prevent sticking together.

For Sauce: Sauté onions, carrot, and garlic for about 5 min. in a non-stick skillet coated with nonfat cooking spray. Add pepper, tomatoes, bay leaf, and thyme. Cook 5 min. more. Add oil. Add fish, if you are using it. Lower heat and cook gently for 15 min., stirring often. Add honey and lemon rind; heat through for 2 min. Spoon over pasta and add vegetable broth seasoning to taste, if desired. Garnish with parsley.
Prep. time: 50 min. *Serves 2.*

Meatless Spaghetti Sauce

1 can (35 oz.) unsalted
Italian tomatoes in
sauce

1 can (6 oz.) unsalted
tomato paste

1 onion, finely diced

½ t. dried basil

½ t. dried oregano

Per Serving		
Total Fat	0.4	gm
Saturated	0.1	gm
Unsaturated	0.3	gm
Cholesterol	0	mg
Sodium	25	mg
Carbohydrate	10	gm
Protein	2	gm
Fiber	2	gm
Calories	44	

Empty tomatoes and tomato paste into a large
saucepan. Add onion, basil, and oregano. Cover and
simmer over low heat for 30 min. Mash tomatoes
into a purée, using a slotted spoon or potato masher.
Use as a sauce for pasta. Makes 5 cups of sauce.
Prep. time: 45 min. *Serves 10.*

Vegetables with Spaghetti

*Lots of kids love this spaghetti recipe. They don't
miss the red sauce because they're perfectly happy
with the mixed vegetables and low-fat cheese sauce.*

1 clove garlic, minced

1 onion, chopped
coarsely

4 T. liquid Butter Buds

1 package (10 oz.) frozen
chopped broccoli,
thawed

1 package (10 oz.) frozen
green peas, thawed

Dash of pepper

8 oz. whole wheat
spaghetti

½ c. grated low-fat,
low-sodium mozzarella
cheese

¼ c. nonfat milk

Per Serving		
Total Fat	5	gm
Saturated	1.7	gm
Unsaturated	3.3	gm
Cholesterol	4	mg
Sodium	293	mg
Carbohydrate	34	gm
Protein	14	gm
Fiber	5	gm
Calories	203	

In large skillet, sauté garlic and onion in Butter Buds
until onion is tender. Add broccoli, peas, and pepper.
Cook, stirring vegetables until tender. Cook spaghetti
according to package directions; drain and toss lightly
with cheese, milk, and vegetables. Serve at once.
Prep. time: 35 min. *Serves 4.*

Spaghetti and Broccoli

Per Serving

Total Fat	8	gm
Saturated	1.1	gm
Unsaturated	6.9	gm
Cholesterol	0 ·	mg
Sodium	49	mg
Carbohydrate	53	gm
Protein	13	gm
Fiber	7	gm
Calories	324	

This is an excellent recipe for anyone who's not accustomed to spaghetti with anything but red sauce. Add one small can of water-packed albacore tuna, if you want, for a whole new taste.

4 oz. uncooked spaghetti (whole grain, if you like)

1 large head or 2 c. cooked broccoli

1 T. olive oil

1 T. vegetable broth seasoning

1 clove fresh garlic, minced

⅛ t. black pepper

Cook spaghetti following package directions. Toss cooked spaghetti, broccoli, oil, and seasonings together. Serve hot.
Prep. time: 20 min. *Serves 2.*

Spaghetti with Italian Tomato Sauce

Per Serving

Total Fat	2	gm
Saturated	0.2	gm
Unsaturated	1.8	gm
Cholesterol	0	mg
Sodium	76	mg
Carbohydrate	79	gm
Protein	14	gm
Fiber	8	gm
Calories	366	

1 brown onion, diced

3 cloves garlic, diced

1 bell pepper, diced

1 c. mushrooms

4 T. water

1 large can (26 oz.) low-sodium tomato purée

1 can (6 oz.) low-sodium tomato paste

⅛ t. oregano

⅛ t. basil

⅛ t. thyme

⅛ t. marjoram

½ lb. (8 oz.) spaghetti, cooked and drained

2 T. grated Parmesan cheese, optional

Sauté onion, garlic, bell pepper, and mushrooms in water until tender. Add tomato purée, tomato paste, and spices. Simmer for 1 hour. Pour over spaghetti. Serve with Parmesan cheese, if desired.
Prep. time: 1 hour and 20 min. *Serves 4.*

Italian Dish with Broccoli

4 oz. linguini, measured
before cooking

1 c. cooked broccoli,
zucchini, mushrooms,
and onion

⅛ t. basil

⅛ t. oregano

½ t. Salt Sub
(see page 235)

6 cherry tomatoes, halved

2 T. grated Parmesan
cheese

Per Serving		
Total Fat	1	gm
Saturated	0.2	gm
Unsaturated	0.8	gm
Cholesterol	0	mg
Sodium	22	mg
Carbohydrate	48	gm
Protein	9	gm
Fiber	2	gm
Calories	235	

Preheat oven to 300° F. Cook linguini according to package directions. Add vegetables and seasonings. Stir in tomatoes. Pour into a non-stick baking dish. Grate cheese over top. Cover and bake for about 15 min., just to mix the flavors and heat through.
Prep. time: 25 min. *Serves 2.*

Spaghetti with Tomato-Cucumber Sauce

4 oz. spaghetti

1 ½ quarts boiling water

1 ½ c. fresh tomatoes,
coarsely chopped

¾ c. cucumber, coarsely
chopped, seeded, pared

1 small clove garlic

¼ t. dried oregano

⅛ t. pepper

Per Serving		
Total Fat	2	gm
Saturated	0.2	gm
Unsaturated	1.8	gm
Cholesterol	0	mg
Sodium	42	mg
Carbohydrate	53	gm
Protein	9	gm
Fiber	3	gm
Calories	259	

Cook spaghetti in boiling water 9-12 min., until tender; drain. Meanwhile, place half of the tomatoes and cucumber, garlic, oregano, and pepper in a blender; process until smooth. Add rest of tomatoes and cucumber to the purée and pour over cooked spaghetti.
Prep. time: 20 min. *Serves 2.*

Pasta Provençale

¼ lb. pasta, cooked and drained

3 red peppers, thinly sliced

3 onions, thinly sliced

½ c. mushrooms, sliced

3 tomatoes, chopped

1 clove garlic, minced

2 c. Salt-Free Chicken Broth (see page 202)

Marjoram, oregano, thyme, and basil to taste

4 packets dry Butter Buds

4 oz. cooked halibut

Cook pasta according to package directions. Sauté peppers, onions, mushrooms, tomatoes, and garlic in non-stick skillet coated with nonfat cooking spray. Dissolve Butter Buds in the chicken broth; add seasoning. Simmer for 25 min. Add cooked halibut. Serve over hot pasta.
Prep. time: 35 min. *Serves 2.*

Stuffed Shells

If you add some gourmet greens to this, it will look and taste as if you've been slaving away in the kitchen for hours.

8 jumbo shells

4 oz. spinach, chopped

4 oz. nonfat ricotta cheese

1 jar (30 oz.) no-salt spaghetti sauce

2 T. grated Parmesan cheese

Preheat oven to 350° F. Cook pasta shells until almost tender. Mix spinach and cheese. Fill pasta shells with spinach-cheese mixture. Place shells in baking pan, open side up. Pour sauce over shells, almost covering with sauce. Cover and bake 45 min. Add Parmesan cheese before serving.
Prep. time: 1 hour and 10 min. *Serves 2.*

8 oz. lasagna noodles

¼ c. water

1 onion, chopped fine

1 clove garlic, minced

1 green pepper, chopped fine

3 c. chopped tomatoes

¼ t. pepper

½ t. dried oregano

1 large zucchini, sliced paper-thin lengthwise

2 c. skim milk ricotta cheese

1 egg white

½ c. shredded Parmesan cheese

Per Serving		
Total Fat	8	gm
Saturated	5	gm
Unsaturated	3	gm
Cholesterol	28	mg
Sodium	167	mg
Carbohydrate	43	gm
Protein	21	gm
Fiber	8	gm
Calories	297	

Preheat oven to 350° F. Cook lasagna noodles until pliable but still firm; rinse under cold water and drain well.

Meanwhile, heat water in a large skillet. Add onion, garlic, green pepper, tomatoes, pepper, and oregano. Cover and simmer 10 min.

Spread a thin layer of sauce over the bottom of a rectangular baking dish. Top with a layer of zucchini, then a layer of cooked lasagna noodles.

Beat ricotta cheese and egg white together; spread half of this mixture over the noodles. Sprinkle with half of the Parmesan cheese. Add another layer of noodles over this; top with remaining cheese mixture and then a layer of noodles. Top with a final layer of zucchini. Spread remaining sauce over top. Sprinkle with remaining Parmesan cheese. Bake for 30 min. Prep. time: 1 hour and 35 min. *Serves 6.*

Lasagna Florentine

*You **will** slave over this recipe, but it will be worth it.*

9 lasagna noodles

1 quart boiling water

½ lb. fresh mushrooms, sliced

2 medium onions, finely diced

2 cloves garlic, finely minced

1 lb. fresh spinach, washed and trimmed

2 c. fresh carrots, coarsely chopped

1 c. skim milk ricotta cheese

1 egg white

1 can (8 oz.) unsalted tomato sauce

3 T. grated Parmesan cheese

Preheat oven to 375° F. Cook noodles in boiling water until almost tender. Drain and rinse to keep noodles separate.

Sauté mushrooms, onions, and garlic in a non-stick skillet coated with nonfat cooking spray. Stir occasionally to keep vegetables from sticking. Add spinach, torn into small bits, and chopped carrots. Cook until spinach is tender, 2-3 min., stirring constantly.

Combine ricotta cheese and egg white, beating well; add to spinach mixture.

Pour a thin layer of tomato sauce over the bottom of a 9 x 13-inch baking dish. Arrange 3 lasagna noodles in dish over sauce. Spread half the spinach mixture in a thin layer over noodles. Sprinkle with 1 T. Parmesan cheese. Top with 3 more lasagna noodles, spread remaining spinach mixture, and sprinkle with 1 T. Parmesan cheese. Arrange final 3 lasagna noodles over top. Pour remaining tomato sauce over all. Sprinkle with remaining Parmesan cheese. Bake for 25 min. Let stand 10 to 15 min. before cutting. Prep. time: 1 hour and 15 min. *Serves 6.*

Eggplant Lasagna

1 medium eggplant, peeled and diced

4 fresh tomatoes, diced

2 stalks celery, sliced

1 small onion, diced

1 clove garlic, diced

1 T. chopped parsley

½ t. dried basil

9 lasagna noodles

1 quart boiling water

½ c. unsalted tomato juice

¼ c. skim milk mozzarella cheese, finely diced

Per Serving		
Total Fat	4	gm
Saturated	2.9	gm
Unsaturated	1.1	gm
Cholesterol	8	mg
Sodium	119	mg
Carbohydrate	58	gm
Protein	15	gm
Fiber	13	gm
Calories	284	

Preheat oven to 350° F. Cook eggplant, tomatoes, celery, onion, garlic, parsley, and basil in a non-stick skillet, stirring frequently, about 10 min. Meanwhile, cook lasagna noodles in boiling water until almost tender; drain and rinse to keep noodles separate.

Place 3 noodles side by side in a greased 9 x 13-inch baking dish. Top with a layer of half the eggplant mixture, then another layer of 3 noodles, then another layer of the remaining eggplant mixture, and finally the last 3 noodles. Pour tomato juice over all. Sprinkle with diced mozzarella cheese. Bake for 25 min. Prep. time: 1 hour and 10 min. *Serves 4.*

Macaroni-Stuffed Eggplant

1 medium eggplant

1 small onion, diced

2 stalks celery, sliced

½ c. unsalted tomato juice

¼ t. oregano

1 c. cooked macaroni

1 T. grated Parmesan cheese

Per Serving		
Total Fat	2	gm
Saturated	0.8	gm
Unsaturated	1.2	gm
Cholesterol	3	mg
Sodium	110	mg
Carbohydrate	46	gm
Protein	8	gm
Fiber	11	gm
Calories	228	

Preheat oven to 350° F. Cut eggplant in half and scoop out flesh carefully, leaving the shells unbroken. Dice scooped out eggplant and place in a saucepan with onion, celery, tomato juice, and oregano. Simmer until tender. Remove from heat and add cooked macaroni. Spoon mixture into eggplant shells. Top with a sprinkling of grated Parmesan cheese. Bake for 20 min. Prep. time: 55 min. *Serves 2.*

Spinach Lasagna

8 oz. uncooked lasagna noodles

1 small eggplant, sliced into paper-thin, round slices

¾ c. unsalted spaghetti sauce

1 T. vegetable broth seasoning

1 large bunch fresh spinach, washed, stems removed

1 t. oregano

12 oz. fresh mushrooms, sliced

1 small onion, chopped

2 T. Parmesan cheese

Preheat oven to 350° F. Cook lasagna noodles in boiling water until almost tender; drain and rinse to keep noodles separate.

Coat a 9 x 14-inch baking dish with nonfat cooking spray. Place one layer of noodles at the bottom of the dish, then one layer of eggplant. Spread this with 4 T. of the spaghetti sauce. Sprinkle with 1 t. of vegetable broth seasoning.

Now place a second layer of lasagna noodles. Heap the spinach over the second layer, about 4 leaves thick. Sprinkle with oregano and another teaspoon of vegetable broth seasoning. Add a thin layer of lasagna noodles. Top with the remainder of the spaghetti sauce, the mushrooms, onions, the last teaspoon of vegetable broth seasoning, and the 2 T. of Parmesan cheese, being careful to sprinkle it lightly so that it will cover the top.

Cover with foil and bake for 45 min. Cut into squares; to serve, layer 2 squares so it will be thicker. The spinach flattens during cooking.
Prep. time: 1 hour and 25 min. *Serves 4.*

Baked Macaroni and Cottage Cheese

4 oz. elbow macaroni

1 ½ quarts boiling water

1 egg white

½ c. skim milk

¾ c. 1% low-fat cottage
cheese

½ t. Worcestershire sauce

⅓ c. chopped onion

⅓ c. celery, chopped

1 T. fresh parsley,
chopped

Per Serving		
Total Fat	3	gm
Saturated	2	gm
Unsaturated	1	gm
Cholesterol	11	mg
Sodium	273	mg
Carbohydrate	56	gm
Protein	28	gm
Fiber	2	gm
Calories	350	

Preheat oven to 350° F. Cook macaroni in boiling
water for 8 min., or until just tender. Beat egg white,
add milk, and stir mixture into cottage cheese. Add
Worcestershire sauce, onion, celery, and parsley. Stir
mixture through cooked macaroni. Pour into a
non-stick baking dish and bake for 35 min., or until
lightly browned.
Prep. time: 55 min. *Serves 2.*

Baked Macaroni and Spinach

8 oz. macaroni

3 quarts boiling water

2 c. unsalted tomato
sauce

1 package (10 oz.) frozen
chopped spinach,
thawed

1 T. grated onion

1 c. skim milk ricotta
cheese

¼ t. nutmeg

⅛ t. pepper

Per Serving		
Total Fat	6	gm
Saturated	3.2	gm
Unsaturated	2.8	gm
Cholesterol	19	mg
Sodium	173	mg
Carbohydrate	59	gm
Protein	18	gm
Fiber	2	gm
Calories	365	

Preheat oven to 350° F. Cook macaroni in boiling
water 9-12 min. until tender; drain. Spoon a layer of
tomato sauce into a small non-stick baking dish.
Then spoon half the macaroni over the bottom of the
baking dish. Top with a mixture of spinach, onion,
ricotta cheese, nutmeg, and pepper. Spoon remaining
macaroni over top. Pour remaining sauce over all.
Bake for 20 min., or until heated through.
Prep. time: 55 min. *Serves 4.*

Macaroni Dinner

1 c. whole wheat elbow macaroni

2 carrots, chopped

¼ t. celery seed

1 can (8 oz.) tomato sauce

1 medium onion, sliced thin

1 package (10 oz.) frozen peas, boiled

1 t. stone-ground mustard

Dash of Tabasco sauce

Pour 2 quarts water into Dutch oven or large pot and heat to simmering. Add macaroni. Cook until tender. Drain off some liquid, until approximately 3 c. remain. Add carrots, celery seed, tomato sauce, and onion. Cook 10 min. Stir in peas, mustard, and hot sauce.

Prep. time: 25 min. *Serves 4.*

Macaroni and Corn

1 small onion, chopped

½ green pepper, chopped

¾ c. unsalted spaghetti sauce

1 package (10 oz.) frozen corn

1 T. vegetable broth seasoning

1 t. olive oil

3 c. cooked macaroni

Sauté onion and green pepper in a medium-sized, non-stick saucepan coated with nonfat cooking spray. Add spaghetti sauce, corn, seasoning, oil, and macaroni. Cook until corn is done, about 10 min. You may add water if you like it soupier.

Prep. time: 25 min. *Serves 2.*

Vegetable-Pasta Casserole

4 oz. spaghetti

1 ½ quarts boiling water

½ c. 1% low-fat cottage cheese

½ c. plain nonfat yogurt

1 c. cut green beans, cooked

1 c. cooked sliced carrots

¼ t. dried dill weed

⅛ t. pepper

Per Serving		
Total Fat	2	gm
Saturated	0.6	gm
Unsaturated	1.4	gm
Cholesterol	4	mg
Sodium	410	mg
Carbohydrate	65	gm
Protein	21	gm
Fiber	4	gm
Calories	358	

Preheat oven to 350° F. Cook spaghetti in boiling water for 9 min. and drain. Combine cottage cheese and yogurt. Place half the spaghetti in a non-stick flat baking dish. Top the spaghetti with half the cheese mixture, then with a layer of beans. Add carrots. Sprinkle with dill weed and pepper. Spread with remaining cheese mixture and top with second half of spaghetti. Bake for 30 min.
Prep. time: 55 min. *Serves 2.*

Rigatoni with Hot Chili Sauce

1 onion, diced

½ t. dried chili peppers

1 clove garlic, finely minced

½ t. chili powder

1 can (8 oz.) tomato sauce

4 oz. rigatoni

1 ½ quarts boiling water

2 T. grated Romano cheese

Dash of pepper

Per Serving		
Total Fat	5	gm
Saturated	2.6	gm
Unsaturated	2.4	gm
Cholesterol	15	mg
Sodium	244	mg
Carbohydrate	64	gm
Protein	15	gm
Fiber	4	gm
Calories	364	

Sauté onion, chili peppers, and garlic in a non-stick skillet, stirring frequently, until onion is limp. Add chili powder and tomato sauce. Cover and simmer for 10 min. Meanwhile, cook rigatoni in boiling water for 9-12 min., or until tender; drain. Toss rigatoni with sauce. Serve with grated cheese and a dash of pepper.
Prep. time: 50 min. *Serves 2.*

Pasta Bow Ties with Yogurt Mushroom Sauce

¼ lb. fresh mushrooms, sliced

1 onion, diced

½ c. Salt-Free Chicken Broth (see page 202)

¼ c. plain nonfat yogurt

⅛ t. pepper

¼ t. dried dill weed

4 oz. pasta bow ties

1 ½ quarts boiling water

Cook mushrooms and onion in a non-stick skillet for a few minutes until limp, stirring frequently. Add chicken broth; cook uncovered until liquid reduces by half. Remove from heat; stir in yogurt, pepper, and dill weed. Meanwhile, cook pasta bow ties in boiling water until tender, about 8 min.; drain. Toss with mushroom sauce; serve.
Prep. time: 20 min. *Serves 2.*

Baked Noodles and Broccoli

1 package (8 oz.) wide noodles, cooked, drained

1 lb. fresh broccoli, cooked, chopped

1 c. skim ricotta cheese

3 scallions, including tops, thinly sliced

1 egg white, beaten

¼ c. whole wheat bread crumbs

2 T. grated Parmesan cheese

Preheat oven to 350° F. Combine cooked noodles and broccoli. Separately, combine ricotta cheese, scallions, and egg white; add noodle-broccoli mixture and toss lightly to mix through. Spoon into a non-stick baking dish. Top with bread crumbs and sprinkle with grated Parmesan cheese. Bake for 30 min.
Prep. time: 50 min. *Serves 4.*

Stuffed Baked Manicotti

1 lb. manicotti pasta
tubes

3 quarts boiling water

3 c. skim milk ricotta
cheese

¼ c. sliced scallions,
including green tops

1 can (16 oz.) tomatoes

2 T. tomato paste

½ t. oregano

¼ t. basil

¼ t. pepper

½ c. whole wheat
bread crumbs

Per Serving		
Total Fat	11	gm
Saturated	6.3	gm
Unsaturated	4.7	gm
Cholesterol	38	mg
Sodium	206	mg
Carbohydrate	70	gm
Protein	25	gm
Fiber	1	gm
Calories	483	

Preheat oven to 350° F. Cook manicotti in boiling
water until pliable, about 7 min. Combine ricotta
cheese and scallions; stuff manicotti tubes with
mixture and place side by side in a non-stick flat
casserole dish. Blend tomatoes, tomato paste,
oregano, basil, and pepper; spoon over stuffed
manicotti. Top with bread crumbs. Bake for 30 min.
Prep. time: 1 hour. *Serves 6.*

Pasta with Shrimp Yogurt Sauce

8 oz. pasta twists

3 quarts boiling water

1 c. plain low-fat yogurt

16 large cooked peeled
shrimp

1 T. sliced scallions

2 T. chopped fresh
parsley

¼ t. Worcestershire sauce

Per Serving		
Total Fat	1	gm
Saturated	0.2	gm
Unsaturated	0.8	gm
Cholesterol	44	mg
Sodium	140	mg
Carbohydrate	48	gm
Protein	16	gm
Fiber	3	gm
Calories	263	

Cook pasta in boiling water until tender, about 9-12
min.; drain. Combine yogurt, 4 shrimp, scallions,
parsley, and Worcestershire sauce in a blender. Cover
and blend until almost smooth. Spoon over hot pasta.
Add remaining whole cooked shrimp and toss.
Prep. time: 25 min. *Serves 4.*

Linguini with Vegetable Garlic Sauce

Here's a way to get the noodles without the egg.

4 oz. linguini

1 ½ quarts boiling water

1 clove garlic, minced

1 c. zucchini, sliced thin

1 c. celery, sliced diagonally

1 green pepper, cut in strips

¼ t. dried basil

⅛ t. pepper

½ c. cherry tomatoes, cut in half

1 T. olive oil

Cook linguini in boiling water until tender, about 9-12 min.; drain. Meanwhile, heat a wok or a non-stick skillet coated with nonfat cooking spray. Add garlic, zucchini, celery, green pepper, basil, and pepper; stir-fry about 5 min., until vegetables are tender but still crisp. Add tomatoes and cook for several minutes more. Add oil. Serve over cooked linguini.
Prep. time: 40 min. *Serves 2.*

Vegeroni Casserole

1 ½ lb. vegeroni (whole grain macaroni with vegetable flour added)

2 small onions, chopped

3 cloves garlic, minced

¾ c. chopped carrot

¾ c. chopped celery

1 c. chopped green pepper

¾ lb. mushrooms, sliced

½ t. black pepper

5 c. tomato sauce

¼ c. grated Parmesan cheese

Preheat oven to 300° F. Cook vegeroni and pour into a non-stick baking dish. Combine remaining ingredients except cheese and pour over noodles. Grate cheese over top. Bake, covered for 30 min. Baked uncovered for 10 min. more.
Prep. time: 1 hour. *Serves 6.*

This recipe calls for olive oil because it doesn't oxidize as quickly as sesame oil. But for authentic Oriental flavor, use crude, expeller-pressed sesame oil in place of the olive oil.

Per Serving		
Total Fat	9	gm
Saturated	1.3	gm
Unsaturated	7.7	gm
Cholesterol	0	mg
Sodium	300	mg
Carbohydrate	79	gm
Protein	17	gm
Fiber	9	gm
Calories	453	

4 oz. fettucine

1 small onion, chopped

8 oz. fresh mushrooms, sliced

2 cloves garlic, minced

1 c. yellow squash, thinly sliced

1 c. zucchini, thinly sliced

1 c. snow peas, strings removed

1 c. fresh bean sprouts

1 c. chopped tomatoes

3 T. liquid Butter Buds

½ c. water

1 T. arrowroot powder

½ t. cayenne pepper

3 T. vegetable broth seasoning

1 T. olive oil

Following package instructions, cook fettucine. Meanwhile, sauté onion, mushrooms, garlic, squash, zucchini, snow peas, sprouts, and tomatoes in a non-stick skillet coated with nonfat cooking spray. Cover and let steam on low.

In a small saucepan, mix together and heat Butter Buds, water and arrowroot powder to make a sauce. Drain cooked pasta and toss with cooked vegetables, sauce, pepper, vegetable broth seasoning, and olive oil. Serve hot.

Prep. time: 35 min. *Serves 2.*

Delicious Pasta with Tuna

Per Serving

Total Fat	6	gm
Saturated	0.9	gm
Unsaturated	5.1	gm
Cholesterol	20	mg
Sodium	541	mg
Carbohydrate	34	gm
Protein	20	gm
Fiber	6	gm
Calories	269	

1 box (8 oz.) pasta (whole wheat if you choose)
1 clove fresh garlic, diced
¼ red onion, chopped
½ c. white wine
1 can (28 oz.) whole tomatoes
1 T. olive oil
1 can (7 oz.) tuna, water packed
1 can (6 oz.) no-salt tomato paste, optional
1 T. fresh parsley

Cook pasta until tender. Meanwhile, coat a non-stick pan with nonfat cooking spray and heat on low. Add garlic and onion. When browned, add ½ c. white wine. Take tomatoes out of can and squeeze juice out of tomatoes. Break tomatoes into pieces and place in pan. Add rest of juice from can. Add oil. Break tuna into small pieces and add to sauce. If you like sauce with a thicker consistency, add tomato paste. When pasta is ready, drain and add to pan with sauce; mix together until pasta is well coated. Sprinkle with fresh parsley.
Prep. time: 30 min. *Serves 4.*

Delicious Pasta with Chicken

Per Serving

Total Fat	8	gm
Saturated	1.3	gm
Unsaturated	6.7	gm
Cholesterol	65	mg
Sodium	399	mg
Carbohydrate	34	gm
Protein	31	gm
Fiber	6	gm
Calories	330	

1 box (8 oz.) pasta (whole wheat if you choose)
1 clove fresh garlic, diced
¼ red onion, chopped
½ c. white wine
1 can (28 oz.) whole tomatoes
1 T. olive oil
8 oz. cooked chicken breast
1 can (6 oz.) no-salt tomato paste, optional
1 T. fresh parsley

Cook pasta until tender. Meanwhile, heat a non-stick, pan-sprayed pan on low. Add garlic and onion. When browned, add white wine. Take tomatoes out of can and squeeze juice out of tomatoes. Break tomatoes into pieces and place in pan. Add rest of juice from can. Add oil. Break chicken into small pieces and add to sauce. If you like sauce with a thicker consistency, add tomato paste. When pasta is ready, drain and add to pan with sauce; mix together until pasta is well coated. Sprinkle with fresh parsley.
Prep. time: 30 min. *Serves 4.*

Delicious Vegetarian Pasta

1 box (8 oz.) pasta (whole wheat if you choose)

1 clove fresh garlic, diced

¼ red onion

½ c. white wine

1 can (28 oz.) whole tomatoes

1 T. olive oil

1 can (6 oz.) no-salt tomato paste, optional

1 T. fresh parsley

Per Serving		
Total Fat	5	gm
Saturated	0.6	gm
Unsaturated	4.4	gm
Cholesterol	0	mg
Sodium	346	mg
Carbohydrate	34	gm
Protein	7	gm
Fiber	6	gm
Calories	201	

Cook pasta until tender. Meanwhile, coat a non-stick pan with nonfat cooking spray and heat on low. Add garlic and onion. When browned, add white wine. Take tomatoes out of can and squeeze juice out of tomatoes. Break tomatoes into pieces and place in pan. Add rest of juice from can. Add oil. If you like sauce with a thicker consistency, add tomato paste. When pasta is ready, drain and add to pan with sauce; mix together until pasta is well coated. Sprinkle with fresh parsley. Prep. time: 30 min. *Serves 4.*

Linguini with Scallops

8 oz. linguini

1 clove garlic, finely minced

1 c. clam juice

1 can (28 oz.) Italian plum tomatoes

½ t. dried thyme

1 T. olive oil

1 lb. bay or sea scallops

Per Serving		
Total Fat	6	gm
Saturated	0.7	gm
Unsaturated	5.3	gm
Cholesterol	60	mg
Sodium	869	mg
Carbohydrate	60	gm
Protein	36	gm
Fiber	3	gm
Calories	436	

Cook linguini as directed on package. Drain. Meanwhile, heat a non-stick skillet coated with nonfat cooking spray; sauté garlic until golden. Add clam juice. Chop tomatoes and add to skillet. Add thyme and oil. About 3 min. before pasta is done, add scallops to the sauce. (If using sea scallops, cut into small pieces.) Cook sauce with scallops about 3 min., or until scallops are opaque. Place drained pasta on a heated serving dish; spoon scallops and sauce over pasta. Prep. time: 35 min. *Serves 4.*

137

Vegetable-Noodle Medley

Per Serving

Total Fat	1	gm
Saturated	0.1	gm
Unsaturated	0.9	gm
Cholesterol	0	mg
Sodium	177	mg
Carbohydrate	37	gm
Protein	8	gm
Fiber	6	gm
Calories	177	

3 c. whole wheat or spinach noodles

2 c. broccoli pieces

1 brown onion

1 stalk celery, chopped

½ T. marjoram

½ T. savory

½ T. basil

1 t. garlic powder

1 T. water

1 T. low-sodium soy sauce

Preheat oven to 350° F. Cook noodles until tender. Steam broccoli, onion, and celery (or any combination of vegetables to equal 3 or 4 c.) until semi-tender. Combine cooked noodles and vegetables. Add seasonings. Mix well. Place in casserole dish. Combine water and soy sauce. Drizzle over top of casserole. Bake for 15 min.
Prep. time: 40 min. *Serves 6.*

Vegetable Lasagna

Per Serving

Total Fat	19	gm
Saturated	2.2	gm
Unsaturated	16.8	gm
Cholesterol	3	mg
Sodium	238	mg
Carbohydrate	65	gm
Protein	19	gm
Fiber	14	gm
Calories	510	

2 jars (32 oz.) no-salt spaghetti sauce

1 t. Italian seasoning

1 t. sweet basil

1 t. garlic powder

1 c. mushrooms, sliced

3 zucchini, sliced

2 boxes (8 oz.) lasagna noodles, cooked

8 oz. nonfat cottage cheese

4 oz. chopped spinach

Preheat oven to 350° F. Cover bottom of a 9 x 13-inch baking dish with sauce. Add ½ t. each of Italian seasoning, sweet basil, and garlic powder. Then, add a layer of noodles, a layer of cheese, and a layer of mushrooms and zucchini. Repeat layers. Pour remaining sauce on top. Top with mushrooms and small amount of cheese for garnish. Bake for 45 min. Cover; let stand for 5 min. before serving.
Prep. time: 40 min. *Serves 6.*

Chicken Tetrazzini Casserole

This is a great recipe for a dinner party. If you try it over rice, all you really need to round things off is a salad.

3 ½ c. Salt-Free Chicken Broth (see page 202)

¼ c. dry white wine

1 c. diced onions

1 c. diced celery

2 T. minced garlic

2 t. basil

½ t. thyme

⅛ t. cayenne pepper

⅛ t. saffron

⅛ t. pepper

1 c. cut carrots

2 c. fresh mushrooms, diced

2 T. canned pimentos, diced

2 c. cooked chicken breasts, diced

1 c. evaporated skim milk

¼ c. whey powder (from health food store)

¼ c. cornstarch

1 T. Parmesan cheese

1 ½ t. minced parsley

2 c. whole wheat spaghetti, cooked, drained

⅛ t. paprika

Per Serving		
Total Fat	8	gm
Saturated	2.3	gm
Unsaturated	5.7	gm
Cholesterol	138	mg
Sodium	322	mg
Carbohydrate	54	gm
Protein	60	gm
Fiber	8	gm
Calories	548	

Preheat oven to 350° F. In a large skillet, heat ½ c. chicken broth and white wine. Sauté onion, celery, and garlic. Add remaining spices and remaining broth and bring to a boil. Add carrots, turn down heat, and simmer until tender. Add mushrooms, pimentos, and chicken. Simmer 5 min.

In a blender, blend milk, whey powder, cornstarch, and cheese. Add mixture to simmering vegetables, stirring occasionally, until thickened. Stir in parsley.

Place cooked spaghetti in a casserole dish and layer chicken and vegetable mixture on top. Sprinkle paprika over spaghetti. Bake for 20 min.
Prep. time: 60 min. *Serves 5.*

Making the switch away from a high-saturated fat, high-cholesterol diet to one that is low-fat, high complex carbohydrate is a wise change indeed.

Over the years, I've found that this healthy diet strategy is a powerful treatment measure for our most serious degenerative diseases—particularly heart disease, diabetes, high blood pressure, and obesity.

Increasing your intake of complex carbohydrates from starches such as pastas, potatoes, breads, corn, and rice is an important part of your diet success. Unfortunately, these starches have been given an undeserved reputation as a cause of obesity. The truth of the matter is that these fat-free foods are the solution to obesity and a host of other health concerns, not the cause.

So stop worrying and enjoy the many delicious, nutritious pasta recipes and other healthy meals in this cookbook!

Main Dishes

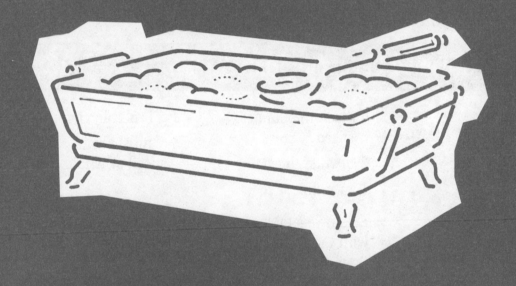

Stuffed Potatoes

These tasty potatoes will fill you up, but won't slow you down.

2 large baking potatoes (about 8 oz. each)

¼ c. farmer cheese, shredded

¼ c. mushrooms, sliced

¼ c. broccoli, chopped

⅛ c. alfalfa sprouts

Bake potatoes at 375° F for 1 hour. Cut top of potato open. Fill with rest of ingredients, starting with the cheese. Serve with soup and salad, if desired.
Prep. time: 1 hour. *Serves 2.*

Steamed Vegetable Platter with Curry Sauce

4 medium potatoes, sliced

2 carrots, sliced

1 zucchini, sliced

2 c. broccoli, chopped

½ c. mushrooms, sliced or whole

Steam vegetables for 10 min. over boiling water. Top with Curry Sauce (see recipe below).
Prep. time: 30 min. *Serves 2.*

Curry Sauce
Tangy curry sauce is a great way to dress up vegetables.

1 c. skim milk

1 c. low-sodium chicken broth

½ c. frozen green peas

1 t. curry

4 t. cornstarch

¼ c. water

Bring skim milk, chicken broth, peas, and curry to a boil. Mix cornstarch and water; add mixture to boiling sauce to thicken.
Prep. time: 10 min. *Serves 2.*

Stir-Fry Vegetables with Hop Suey Sauce

Quick and easy, this recipe is a delightful mix of colorful veggies and oriental spices.

½ c. celery, chopped

½ c. carrots, chopped

1 large onion, chopped

2 cloves garlic, minced

1 t. fresh ginger root, grated

1 c. red and green bell peppers, chopped

½ c. zucchini or yellow squash, sliced

½ c. broccoli

½ c. cauliflower

½ c. bean sprouts

½ c. napa cabbage

½ c. almonds

4 c. cooked brown rice

Cook vegetables quickly in a wok or hot pan coated with nonfat cooking spray, starting with vegetables that take longest to cook (celery, carrots, onions). Add almonds. Season with Hop Suey Sauce (see recipe below) to taste. Serve over hot rice or noodles, if desired.
Prep. time: 50 min. *Serves 2.*

Hop Suey Sauce

1 c. Salt-Free Chicken Broth (see page 202)

1 T. low-sodium soy sauce

1 T. arrowroot

Mix ingredients together.
Prep. time: 10 min. *Serves 2.*

Stir-Fry Vegetables with Ginger Sauce

Per Serving

Total Fat	19	gm
Saturated	1.7	gm
Unsaturated	17.3	gm
Cholesterol	0	mg
Sodium	834	mg
Carbohydrate	40	gm
Protein	18	gm
Fiber	12	gm
Calories	378	

Toasted almonds give this stir-fry recipe a mellow, crunchy taste you'll love.

3 c. chopped zucchini

1 onion, chopped

1 red bell pepper, chopped

½ c. celery, chopped

1 c. bean sprouts

1 c. napa cabbage

½ c. toasted almonds

In large, hot pan coated with nonfat cooking spray, cook all vegetables except bean sprouts and cabbage. Cook until tender, about 5 min. Add sprouts and cabbage. Top with Ginger Sauce (see recipe below) to taste. Sprinkle with toasted almonds before serving. **Note:** Toast almonds on cookie sheet for about 10 min. at 375° F.

Prep. time: 40 min. *Serves 2.*

Ginger Sauce

1 clove garlic

1 ½ c. Salt-Free Chicken Broth (see page 202)

2 T. dry sherry

1 t. ginger

2 T. low-sodium soy sauce

1 T. cornstarch

¼ t. water

Sauté garlic in a little chicken broth. Add rest of broth, sherry, ginger, and soy sauce. Simmer on low heat for a few min. Mix cornstarch with water and add to sauce. Heat to desired consistency.

Prep. time: 15 min. *Serves 2.*

Yogurt-Topped Baked Potatoes

For an extra treat and an elegant touch, top your potato with chopped chives

1 c. nonfat yogurt

½ c. minced seeded cucumber

1 t. dill weed

Pinch of white pepper

½ c. green onions, chopped

2 large baking potatoes (about 10 oz. each)

Per Serving		
Total Fat	0.3	gm
Saturated	0.1	gm
Unsaturated	0.2	gm
Cholesterol	3	mg
Sodium	104	mg
Carbohydrate	82	gm
Protein	13	gm
Fiber	7	gm
Calories	377	

Preheat oven to 350° F. Combine all ingredients except potatoes and chill for 2 hours. Bake potatoes for 1 hour. Slit top of potatoes and fill with chilled mixture.

Prep. time: 1 hour and 20 min. *Serves 2.*

Vegetable Tostada

When you crave Mexican...

2 c. cooked pinto beans

½ onion, chopped

2 whole wheat tortillas

½ head lettuce, shredded

1 carrot, shredded

½ c. green bell pepper, chopped

½ c. tomatoes, chopped

2 t. nonfat plain yogurt

½ c. salsa

Per Serving		
Total Fat	3	gm
Saturated	2.2	gm
Unsaturated	0.8	gm
Cholesterol	2	mg
Sodium	607	mg
Carbohydrate	80	gm
Protein	21	gm
Fiber	19	gm
Calories	422	

Preheat oven to 350° F. Purée beans and onion. Toast tortillas for about 5 min. Spread beans on tortillas and add lettuce, carrot, pepper and tomatoes. Top tortillas with yogurt and salsa.

Prep. time: 25 min. *Serves 2.*

Oriental Noodles

Per Serving

Total Fat	3	gm
Saturated	0.6	gm
Unsaturated	2.4	gm
Cholesterol	0	mg
Sodium	1108	mg
Carbohydrate	89	gm
Protein	19	gm
Fiber	4	gm
Calories	424	

Buckwheat is not wheat at all, but comes from an herbaceous plant cultivated specifically for its triangular seeds. The seeds are extremely versatile and make great pancakes as well as great noodles. See for yourself!

3 packages (12 oz. each) buckwheat noodles

4 T. low-sodium soy sauce

1 T. ginger

2 c. celery, cut in long, thin strips

1 large onion, cut in long, thin strips

4 c. bean sprouts

2 c. pea pods, uncut

1 c. water chestnuts

1 c. mushrooms, sliced

1 T. olive oil

1 t. sesame oil

1 c. Salt-Free Chicken Broth (see page 202)

1 T. cornstarch

Preheat oven to 400° F. Boil noodles until tender, being careful not to overcook. Rinse noodles with cold water.

In a large bowl, mix noodles with 2 T. soy sauce and ginger. Spread noodles on a cookie sheet coated with nonfat cooking spray and bake for 15 min.

While noodles are baking, stir-fry (low to medium heat) the celery, onion, sprouts, pea pods, and water chestnuts in a pan-sprayed wok for about 5 min.

In a separate pan coated with nonfat cooking spray, brown mushrooms. Add the mushrooms to the stir-fry vegetables. Then mix in olive oil and ½ t. sesame oil. Add chicken broth and cornstarch; simmer for 5 min.

In a large bowl, combine noodles with the vegetable mixture. Add 2 T. soy sauce and ½ t. sesame oil; combine thoroughly. Serve immediately on a large dinner plate.
Prep. time: 1 hour. *Serves 10.*

Stuffed Green Peppers with Rice and Sauce

This recipe makes a beautiful gourmet dish, perfect for company. Once you've put the peppers in the oven, you can relax.

2 c. brown rice, cooked

2 T. sunflower seeds, raw, hulled

1 carrot, grated

1 onion, chopped

1 jar unsalted spaghetti sauce (26 oz.)

2 t. vegetable broth seasoning

2 large, cored green peppers, presteamed to soften

1 t. Parmesan cheese

Per Serving		
Total Fat	26	gm
Saturated	3.5	gm
Unsaturated	22.5	gm
Cholesterol	1	mg
Sodium	139	mg
Carbohydrate	104	gm
Protein	18	gm
Fiber	20	gm
Calories	729	

Preheat oven to 350° F. Combine cooked brown rice with sunflower seeds, grated carrot, chopped onion, and unsalted spaghetti sauce. Add vegetable broth seasoning. Fill peppers with rice mixture and top with cheese. Stand upright in a casserole dish. Cover and bake for 30 to 40 min., or until heated through. Serve with extra rice and spaghetti sauce, if desired. Prep. time: 1 hour. *Serves 2.*

The Italians are known for roasting their peppers over a flame. First they gut the peppers, then hold them with tongs, close to the fire, until they blacken. Their high water content keeps the peppers from catching fire. When thoroughly blackened and cooled, the skin can be rubbed off. This kind of preparation is quite a bit of work, but you may find the flavor well worth it.

Eggplant Gina

The optional topping makes this a complete dinner, but it's still light and fresh.

1 medium eggplant, (about 19 oz.) sliced lengthwise into 12 slices

1 small onion, chopped

1 T. oregano

1 T. vegetable broth seasoning

2 T. hulled sunflower seeds

1 jar (16 oz.) unsalted spaghetti sauce

1 T. vegetable broth seasoning

Bread crumbs and grated Parmesan cheese or grated mozzarella cheese, optional

Preheat oven to 400° F. Layer ingredients in a 9 x 14-inch casserole dish in the order given. Cover and bake for 45 m Top with bread crumbs, Parmesan cheese or grated mozzarella cheese, if desired.
Prep. time: 1 hour. *Serves 2.*

Oriental Dinner

½ large green pepper, sliced

1 stalk celery, chopped (about 1 c.)

¼ lb. snow peas, deveined

½ small onion, chopped

¼ lb. mung sprouts

4 oz. fresh mushrooms, sliced

1 T. sliced canned pimentos, for color

1 ¼ c. water

1 T. arrowroot flour

1 T. olive oil

1 T. low-sodium soy sauce

1 T. vegetable broth seasoning

½ of an 8 oz. can of sliced water chestnuts

2 c. cooked rice

In a non-stick skillet coated with nonfat cooking spray, sauté green pepper, celery, snow peas, onion, sprouts, mushrooms, and pimento (in this order). It will take approximately 15 min. Next, mix ¼ c. water with arrowroot and stir into skillet. Allow vegetables to cook 5 min. more. Remove from heat and add olive oil. Combine remaining 1 c. of water with soy sauce and vegetable broth seasoning; add to vegetable mixture. Top with water chestnuts. Serve over rice.
Prep. time: 55 min. *Serves 2.*

Ratatouille Especiál

2 c. water

2 c. eggplant, cut in half-inch chunks

1 c. zucchini, cut in chunks

½ c. green pepper, cut in chunks

½ c. onion, cut in chunks

1 c. cooked mushrooms

3 T. unsalted spaghetti sauce

2 T. vegetable broth seasoning

4 c. cooked brown rice

Per Serving		
Total Fat	3	gm
Saturated	0.5	gm
Unsaturated	2.5	gm
Cholesterol	0	mg
Sodium	14	mg
Carbohydrate	60	gm
Protein	7	gm
Fiber	7	gm
Calories	285	

In a large pot, combine water with remaining ingredients, except rice. Cook 30 min. over medium-low heat, until green pepper is tender. Serve over hot cooked rice.
Prep. time: 50 min. *Serves 4.*

Enchiladas Ricardo

This is a great "make ahead" meal to come home to after the game or just after a busy day.

1 can (6 oz.) tomato paste

24 oz. water

1 T. Salt Sub (see page 235)

3 c. cooked navy, kidney, or pinto beans

1 c. carrot, shredded

1 c. frozen corn, thawed

4 oz. fresh mushrooms, chopped

3 peeled tomatoes, chopped

4 T. vegetable broth seasoning

1 dozen corn tortillas

3 T. Parmesan cheese, grated

Per Serving		
Total Fat	4	gm
Saturated	1	gm
Unsaturated	3	gm
Cholesterol	2	mg
Sodium	203	mg
Carbohydrate	63	gm
Protein	16	gm
Fiber	11	gm
Calories	336	

Preheat oven to 500° F. Mix tomato paste with water and Salt Sub. Separately, combine beans, carrot, corn, mushrooms, tomatoes, and vegetable broth seasoning. Dip tortillas in tomato paste mixture and lay flat on a non-stick cookie sheet coated with nonfat cooking spray. Fill each with bean mixture. Fold each tortilla over and fasten with a toothpick driven in at an angle. Grate cheese over top. Bake for 15 min.
Prep. time: 45 min. *Serves 6.*

Chow Mein

Per Serving

Total Fat	18	gm
Saturated	2.6	gm
Unsaturated	15.4	gm
Cholesterol	0	mg
Sodium	261	mg
Carbohydrate	48	gm
Protein	8	gm
Fiber	5	gm
Calories	369	

This is a tasty crowd pleaser. You may want to make twice as much so you can enjoy delicious leftovers.

1 c. snow peas

1 small can water chestnuts

8 oz. fresh mushrooms, sliced

1 carrot, chopped

2 T. water

2 T. arrowroot

2 c. Salt-Free Chicken Broth (see page 202)

1 package chow mein noodles

1 T. low-sodium soy sauce

1 T. Salt Sub (see page 235)

Stir-fry snow peas, water chestnuts, mushrooms, and carrot in a pan coated with nonfat cooking spray. Add water and simmer 20 min., or until the carrot is tender. Combine arrowroot with chicken broth. Add to vegetables and cook until just thickened. Serve over chow mein noodles. Season at the table with low-sodium soy sauce and Salt Sub.
Prep. time: 50 min. *Serves 4.*

Rice-Stuffed Peppers

Per Serving

Total Fat	1	gm
Saturated	0.2	gm
Unsaturated	0.8	gm
Cholesterol	0	mg
Sodium	11	mg
Carbohydrate	36	gm
Protein	5	gm
Fiber	5	gm
Calories	168	

1 c. brown rice

1 onion, minced

2 T. parsley, chopped

1 clove garlic, minced

Dash of sage and thyme

6 large bell peppers

1 ½ c. fresh tomato pulp

Preheat oven to 350° F. Steam rice according to package directions. Sauté onion, parsley, and garlic in a non-stick skillet coated with nonfat cooking spray. Combine with rice and seasonings. Cut tops off peppers and dice. Clean out seeds and fill with rice mixture. Place in casserole dish. Blend tomato pulp with diced pepper and pour over all. Bake for 30 to 40 min.
Prep. time: 1 hour. *Serves 6.*

Good, old-fashioned pizza in a fresh, hot, healthy way.

1 package live yeast

1 c. warm water

2 t. baking powder

2 T. liquid Butter Buds

2 T. honey

2 ½ c. whole wheat flour

4 servings Italian Spaghetti Sauce (see page 234)

2 t. Salt Sub (see page 235)

½ large onion, chopped

½ bell pepper, chopped

1 c. mushrooms, sliced

2 oz. grated Parmesan or skim milk mozzarella cheese

Per Serving		
Total Fat	3	gm
Saturated	1.2	gm
Unsaturated	1.8	gm
Cholesterol	5	mg
Sodium	168	mg
Carbohydrate	65	gm
Protein	14	gm
Fiber	12	gm
Calories	319	

Preheat oven to 425° F. Make crust by dissolving yeast in warm water; add baking powder, Butter Buds, and honey; work into the flour until a thick bread-dough consistency is reached.

Roll the dough onto a pizza pan heavily coated with nonfat cooking spray. Let rise for 15 min. Flatten with your hands (thickness is a matter of preference).

Bake the crust for 10 min. or until browned. Spoon spaghetti sauce onto crust and top with Salt Sub, onion, pepper, mushrooms, and grated cheese. Bake for an additional 5 to 10 min., or until done.
Prep. time: 1 hour and 10 min. Makes 1 large or 2 small pizzas. *Serves 6 to 8.*

Vegetable Cutlets with Tangy Sauce

Per Serving		
Total Fat	2	gm
Saturated	1.8	gm
Unsaturated	0.2	gm
Cholesterol	0	mg
Sodium	120	mg
Carbohydrate	47	gm
Protein	10	gm
Fiber	7	gm
Calories	235	

You might want to make the tangy sauce first so it can simmer while you're putting the rest of this delectable dish together.

1 c. mushrooms, finely diced

⅔ c. green beans, cut to ½-inch lengths

2 c. asparagus, cut to ½-inch lengths

1 c. celery, finely chopped

¼ c. frozen corn, thawed

1 ¼ c. carrots, grated

¾ c. onions, diced

⅓ c. frozen peas, thawed

¾ t. mustard powder

¼ t. ginger

1 ¼ c. matzo meal

2 egg whites, stiffly beaten

Preheat oven to 350° F. Steam mushrooms, green beans, asparagus, celery, and corn about 5 to 10 min., or until tender. In a mixing bowl, combine steamed vegetables with remaining ingredients, trying not to mash the vegetables. Form into patties, place onto a non-stick baking sheet and cover with foil. Bake for 20 min. Uncover and bake to brown another 15 min. Serve with Tangy Sauce (see recipe below).
Prep. time: 1 hour and 10 min. *Serves 6.*

Tangy Sauce

2 c. tomato sauce

4 peeled crushed tomatoes

1 T. prepared mustard

1 T. coriander

2 t. Salt Sub (see page 235)

½ to 1 whole minced green chili pepper

⅛ t. allspice

Combine all ingredients in a saucepan and bring to a boil. Simmer for one hour. Makes about 2 cups.
Prep. time: 1 hour and 10 min. *Serves 6.*

Stuffed Green Peppers á la Raffaele

4 large green bell peppers

2 c. brown rice, cooked

6 c. water

4 medium carrots, grated

4 medium tomatoes, peeled and chopped

¾ lb. mushrooms, chopped

¼ c. raw sunflower seeds, shelled, unsalted

½ c. parsley leaves, chopped

4 t. Salt Sub (see page 235)

Per Serving		
Total Fat	7	gm
Saturated	0.8	gm
Unsaturated	6.2	gm
Cholesterol	0	mg
Sodium	58	mg
Carbohydrate	49	gm
Protein	10	gm
Fiber	10	gm
Calories	273	

Preheat oven to 350° F. Cook bell peppers by removing the caps and seeds, turning ends up in a pot filled with 1 inch of water. Steam about 10 to 15 min., or until tender. Mix remaining ingredients together; stuff peppers with mixture. Peppers can be stuffed whole or halved. Bake in a covered baking dish for 20 min.
Prep. time: 1 hour. *Serves 4.*

Squash Supreme over Rice

Try this in the fall, when the squash are full and ripe.

2 zucchini, chopped

2 yellow crookneck squash, chopped

1 small tomato, chopped fine

1 scallion, white part only, chopped

⅛ t. basil

1 t. Salt Sub (see page 235)

2 c. brown rice, cooked

Per Serving		
Total Fat	1	gm
Saturated	0.2	gm
Unsaturated	0.8	gm
Cholesterol	0	mg
Sodium	13	mg
Carbohydrate	17	gm
Protein	4	gm
Fiber	6	gm
Calories	79	

Mix all ingredients, except rice, and simmer over medium heat about 5 to 10 min., or until tender. Serve hot over cooked brown rice.
Prep. time: 25 min. *Serves 2.*

Potato, Onion, and Leek Casserole Pie

Per Serving

Total Fat	4	gm
Saturated	0.6	gm
Unsaturated	3.4	gm
Cholesterol	0	mg
Sodium	42	mg
Carbohydrate	83	gm
Protein	14	gm
Fiber	8	gm
Calories	400	

3-4 medium potatoes, quartered, with skin on

3 brown onions, peeled and quartered

3 leeks, sliced into 1-inch circles

1 bay leaf

1 c. wheat germ

1 t. garlic powder

1 T. parsley flakes

½ T. savory

Preheat oven to 350° F. Steam potatoes, onions, and leeks until tender. Add bay leaf to water. Mash slightly with potato masher. Add remaining ingredients. Mix well. Place in casserole dish. Bake for 20 to 30 min.
Prep. time: 50 min. *Serves 2.*

Vegetable Casserole

Per Serving

Total Fat	5	gm
Saturated	0.1	gm
Unsaturated	4.9	gm
Cholesterol	10	mg
Sodium	631	mg
Carbohydrate	49	gm
Protein	17	gm
Fiber	15	gm
Calories	300	

1 lb. eggplant

¼ c. liquid Butter Buds

½ c. onion, chopped

1 clove garlic, crushed

½ green pepper, cut in strips

2 c. stewed tomatoes

1 can (8 oz.) red kidney beans, drained and rinsed

1 t. chili powder

Pinch pepper

½ c. lettuce, shredded

1 oz. Parmesan cheese, shredded

Preheat oven to 325° F. Cut eggplant into 1-inch cubes. Sauté Butter Buds, onion, garlic, and green pepper. Cook and stir for 5 min. Add tomatoes, beans, chili powder, and pepper. Stir in eggplant and pour into small casserole dish. Bake for 45 min. Ladle into soup bowls and add lettuce and cheese.
Prep. time: 1 hour and 10 min. *Serves 2.*

Everyone loves this recipe, even the kids, because it's so rich. Once you try it, you'll make it again and again.

Per Serving		
Total Fat	7	gm
Saturated	0.9	gm
Unsaturated	6.1	gm
Cholesterol	0	mg
Sodium	519	mg
Carbohydrate	64	gm
Protein	16	gm
Fiber	12	gm
Calories	365	

Filling:

1 onion, chopped

1 bell pepper, chopped

1 stalk celery, chopped

1 clove garlic, minced

1 t. olive oil

2 c. tomato sauce

3 c. cooked mashed pinto beans

2 c. corn, fresh or frozen

1 ½ t. chili powder

1 can (4 oz.) black olives, sliced or chopped

1 c. hoop cheese or tofu, crumbled

Crust:

1 c. stone-ground cornmeal

1 c. cold water

½ t. Salt Sub (see page 235)

1 c. boiling water

1 t. olive oil

Preheat oven to 350° F. In a non-stick pan coated with nonfat cooking spray, sauté onion, pepper, celery, and garlic. Take off heat and add oil. Blend tomato sauce, pinto beans, corn, chili powder, and olives with sautéed vegetables. Pour into baking dish. Top with hoop cheese or tofu.

To make pie crust, blend cornmeal with cold water. Add Salt Sub to boiling water. Now add cold water-cornmeal mixture to boiling-water mixture and stir until thickened. Mix in oil. Spread cornmeal mixture evenly over casserole dish and bake uncovered for 40 to 50 min.

Prep. time: 1 hour and 45 min. *Serves 6.*

Potato-Vegetable Scallop

Per Serving

Total Fat	5	gm
Saturated	2.1	gm
Unsaturated	2.9	gm
Cholesterol	1	mg
Sodium	125	mg
Carbohydrate	27	gm
Protein	4	gm
Fiber	5	gm
Calories	160	

8 oz. frozen crinkle-cut french fried potatoes
1 c. zucchini, thinly sliced
¼ c. onions, chopped
¼ c. green peppers, chopped
½ t. garlic, finely chopped
1 T. liquid Butter Buds
1 t. whole wheat flour

½ lb. fresh tomatoes, cut in wedges
Pinch marjoram
Pinch white pepper
Pinch celery seed
1 T. grated Parmesan cheese
1 c. whole wheat bread crumbs

Preheat oven to 350° F. Remove potatoes from freezer and set aside. Sauté zucchini, onions, peppers, and garlic in Butter Buds. Stir and cook about 8 min. Sprinkle flour over vegetables. Add remaining ingredients, except cheese and bread crumbs. Mix well. Bring to a boil and remove from heat. Place half of potatoes into shallow baking dish top with hot vegetable mixture. Spread evenly. Heap remaining potatoes on top. Leave 1-inch border of vegetable mixture. Bake for 40 min. Sprinkle cheese and bread crumbs over potatoes during last 10 min. of baking.
Prep. time: 1 hour and 20 min. *Serves 4.*

Engalian Pizzas

Per Serving

Total Fat	8	gm
Saturated	2.9	gm
Unsaturated	5.1	gm
Cholesterol	7	mg
Sodium	594	mg
Carbohydrate	65	gm
Protein	14	gm
Fiber	8	gm
Calories	385	

Engalian Pizzas are great for children because they get to have the taste they crave.

4 whole grain English muffins, halved
8 T. unsalted spaghetti sauce (about ⅓ of a 16 oz. jar)
¼ small onion, finely chopped

8 slices green pepper, very thin
8 T. cooked, sliced mushrooms
8 t. grated Parmesan cheese

Preheat oven to 350° F. Place the halved muffins on a non-stick cookie sheet. Top each with 1 T. spaghetti sauce, 2 t. of onion, 1 slice of green pepper, and 1 T. mushrooms. Sprinkle 1 t. grated cheese evenly over the top. Bake for 15 min.
Prep. time: 30 min. *Serves 2.*

Make this ahead of time and pop it in the oven when you're ready. If your goal is to be a complete vegetarian, but you're only beginning, try using ½ cup of ground white chicken or turkey meat instead of the walnuts. Gradually wean yourself from the meat until you're using just walnuts. This recipe has so much flavor—you'll hardly notice the difference.

Per Serving		
Total Fat	6	gm
Saturated	0.7	gm
Unsaturated	5.3	gm
Cholesterol	0	mg
Sodium	134	mg
Carbohydrate	24	gm
Protein	35	gm
Fiber	2	gm
Calories	167	

1 can (16 oz.) green beans (no salt)

1 c. liquid from green beans

1 egg white

¾ c. cooked brown rice or barley

2 T. vegetable broth seasoning

¼ c. raw walnut pieces (approximately ⅛ c. if chopped)

2 T. unsalted spaghetti sauce

2 cloves garlic

¼ c. cooked mushrooms

2 c. whole wheat bread crumbs, packed (4 slices of bread)

Preheat oven to 300° F. Blend green beans with their liquid in the blender. Add remaining ingredients, except the bread crumbs, and blend. Put bread crumbs in the bottom of a bowl, cover with mixture and stir. Pour into a non-stick loaf pan. Bake for 45 min. Prep. time: 1 hour and 15 min. *Serves 4.*

When you go to the grocery store, shop around the periphery of the store first. That's where you'll find all the fresh produce and since unprocessed food is always less expensive, that's where you'll find the best buys, too.

Green Pepper and Pineapple Skewers

Per Serving

Total Fat	0.4 gm
Saturated	0 gm
Unsaturated	0.4 gm
Cholesterol	0 mg
Sodium	8 mg
Carbohydrate	31 gm
Protein	2 gm
Fiber	4 gm
Calories	120

Here's a colorful backyard barbecue treat for summer parties. Have guests thread their own skewers to get involved.

3 T. tomato paste

3 T. honey

2 T. cider vinegar

⅛ t. cinnamon

⅛ t. cloves

⅛ t. allspice

1 can (16 oz.) unsweetened pineapple chunks

3 large green peppers, cut into 2-inch chunks

Combine tomato paste, honey, vinegar, and spices. Marinate green pepper chunks and pineapple in this mixture for 30 to 60 min. Thread pineapple and pepper chunks alternately on skewers. (Since skewers vary in length, the number used varies.) Barbecue on an outdoor barbecue or under a broiler, turning often. Prep. time: 30 min., plus marinating time. *Serves 3.*

Zucchini Casserole

Per Serving

Total Fat	2 gm
Saturated	0.2 gm
Unsaturated	1.8 gm
Cholesterol	0 mg
Sodium	30 mg
Carbohydrate	20 gm
Protein	3 gm
Fiber	3 gm
Calories	98

1 large zucchini, cut into ½-inch slices

½ onion, diced

2 small pink potatoes, unpeeled and diced

4 oz. fresh mushrooms, sliced

1 stalk celery, chopped

1 can (16 oz.) Italian tomatoes, diced

1 T. vegetable broth seasoning

1 t. crushed basil leaves

1 t. olive oil

Preheat oven to 350° F. Combine the fresh vegetables in a non-stick casserole dish. Add vegetable broth seasoning and basil leaves. Cover with casserole lid and cook in oven for 1 hour. Remove from oven and mix in olive oil.
Prep. time: 1 hour and 30 min. *Serves 4.*

1 c. cooked pinto beans

1 c. unsalted spaghetti sauce

1 c. salsa (mild or hot according to taste preference)

1 c. cooked brown rice

2 T. vegetable broth seasoning

¼ c. chopped onions

6 corn tortillas

1 T. Parmesan cheese, grated

Per Serving		
Total Fat	12	gm
Saturated	4.2	gm
Unsaturated	7.8	gm
Cholesterol	5	mg
Sodium	1023	mg
Carbohydrate	100	gm
Protein	21	gm
Fiber	17	gm
Calories	593	

Preheat oven to 350° F. Blend pinto beans, ⅔ c. spaghetti sauce, and ⅓ c. salsa coarsely in the blender. Transfer to a bowl and add rice, 1 T. vegetable broth seasoning, and onions. Put 2 heaping T. of the mixture into each corn tortilla and roll up. Place side by side in a non-stick 6 x 10-inch baking dish. In a bowl, mix remaining spaghetti sauce, salsa, and vegetable broth seasoning; pour evenly over rolled tortillas. Sprinkle Parmesan cheese over all. Cover with foil and seal. Bake for 30 min.
Prep. time: 1 hour and 15 min. *Serves 2.*

Sweet Potato Casserole

Try this for a sweet twist on potatoes, especially welcome on holidays.

2 sweet potatoes (about 12 oz. each)

1 T. orange juice

1 T. lemon juice

1 t. grated orange peel

¼ c. raisins

1 apple, cored and sliced

1 T. cornstarch

Per Serving		
Total Fat	1	gm
Saturated	0.1	gm
Unsaturated	0.9	gm
Cholesterol	0	mg
Sodium	17	mg
Carbohydrate	75	gm
Protein	4	gm
Fiber	7	gm
Calories	297	

Preheat oven to 400° F. Bake sweet potatoes for 45 min. Cool and remove from skin. Cut into pieces and place in casserole dish. In a separate pan, mix orange juice, lemon juice, grated orange peel, raisins and apple slices. Bring to boil and thicken with cornstarch. Pour over sweet potatoes and return to oven for 30 min. at 350° F.
Prep. time: 55 min. *Serves 2.*

Ratatouille-Topped Baked Potatoes

Per Serving

Total Fat	1	gm
Saturated	0.2	gm
Unsaturated	0.8	gm
Cholesterol	0	mg
Sodium	148	mg
Carbohydrate	85	gm
Protein	10	gm
Fiber	14	gm
Calories	365	

With very little effort, this recipe lets you make an extraordinary meal out of plain old potatoes.

2-3 Idaho potatoes (Russets)

3 T. liquid Butter Buds

½ eggplant, cut in 1-inch cubes

¼ c. red onion, chopped

1-2 cloves garlic, minced

1 small green pepper, cut in 1-inch cubes

1 small red pepper, cut in 1-inch cubes

1 tomato, cut in 1-inch cubes

¼ c. water

½ c. cut green beans

1 zucchini, cut in strips

½ c. fresh mushrooms

Preheat oven to 425° F. Scrub potatoes, dry, and prick with a fork. Bake for 1 hour. To make sauce, heat Butter Buds in large skillet over moderate heat. Add eggplant, onion and garlic. Sauté 1 minute. Add green and red pepper, cook 1 minute longer. Add tomatoes and water. Simmer 3 min. Just before serving, add beans, zucchini, and mushrooms. Heat through. When potatoes are cooked, cut an "X" into the top and push up with fingers. Spoon sauce over potatoes.
Prep. time: 1 hour. *Serves 2.*

Zucchini-Eggplant-Tomato Casserole

Per Serving

Total Fat	2	gm
Saturated	0.2	gm
Unsaturated	1.8	gm
Cholesterol	0	mg
Sodium	36	mg
Carbohydrate	39	gm
Protein	7	gm
Fiber	13	gm
Calories	175	

1 medium eggplant, peeled and cubed

3 zucchini, cubed

1 large onion, sliced

3 tomatoes, coarsely chopped

5 T. fresh tomato pulp

3 cloves garlic, chopped

½ t. oregano

Preheat oven to 300° F. Sauté eggplant and zucchini until lightly browned in a pan coated with nonfat cooking spray. Combine with remaining ingredients. Simmer until onions are limp. Place in casserole dish and bake for 1 hour.
Prep. time: 1 hour and 25 minutes. *Serves 2.*

Grilled Chicken Teriyaki

2 boneless chicken breast halves

2 c. cooked brown rice

¼ c. low-sodium soy sauce

½ c. water

2 T. apple juice concentrate

1 t. rice vinegar

4 c. sliced mushrooms

Garlic to taste

Per Serving		
Total Fat	10	gm
Saturated	2.6	gm
Unsaturated	7.4	gm
Cholesterol	83	mg
Sodium	1,148	mg
Carbohydrate	62	gm
Protein	40	gm
Fiber	5	gm
Calories	497	

Grill chicken breast halves. To make teriyaki sauce, mix remaining ingredients, except rice. Simmer about 15 min. Place grilled chicken on rice and pour teriyaki sauce over chicken.
Prep. time: 30 min. *Serves 2.*

Chicken Italian

If you mix the sauce the night before and let it sit, the spices have a better chance to blend. Try it. You'll love it.

1 onion, chopped

1 bell pepper, sliced

1 zucchini, sliced

1 clove garlic, minced

2 chicken breast halves, cooked and chopped

4 c. Italian Spaghetti Sauce (see page 234)

1 t. basil

1 t. Italian spice

1 t. olive oil

2 c. cooked brown rice

Per Serving		
Total Fat	5	gm
Saturated	1	gm
Unsaturated	4	gm
Cholesterol	44	mg
Sodium	117	mg
Carbohydrate	42	gm
Protein	25	gm
Fiber	11	gm
Calories	297	

Sauté onion, bell pepper, zucchini, and garlic in a non-stick pan coated with nonfat cooking spray. Add chopped chicken, spaghetti sauce, and seasonings, and simmer on low heat for 30 min. Remove from heat and add olive oil. Serve over brown rice.
Prep. time: 55 min. *Serves 2.*

Baked Chicken and Pineapple

Per Serving

Total Fat	8	gm
Saturated	2.2	gm
Unsaturated	5.8	gm
Cholesterol	83	mg
Sodium	100	mg
Carbohydrate	18	gm
Protein	30	gm
Fiber	1	gm
Calories	267	

Baked pineapple is soft and sweet; you'll be pleasantly surprised.

4 chicken breast halves, skin removed

1 can (13 ½ oz.) unsweetened pineapple chunks in juice

½ c. whole wheat bread crumbs

2 T. fresh parsley, chopped

¼ t. ground ginger

¼ t. nutmeg

Preheat oven to 350° F. Dip chicken breasts in pineapple juice. Combine bread crumbs, parsley, ginger, and nutmeg. Coat chicken with this mixture. Place in a flat non-stick baking pan. Spoon pineapple chunks around chicken pieces and pour remaining juice over all. Bake for 1 hour.
Prep. time: 1 hour and 25 min. *Serves 4.*

Chicken Salad with Grapes

Per Serving

Total Fat	25	gm
Saturated	2.8	gm
Unsaturated	22.2	gm
Cholesterol	68	mg
Sodium	231	mg
Carbohydrate	38	gm
Protein	44	gm
Fiber	8	gm
Calories	530	

This is a great lunch or a light supper, good for guests if you increase the recipe.

1 boneless breast of chicken, chopped

½ apple, chopped

½ c. seedless green grapes, halved

2 T. almonds

2 T. sunflower seeds

½ c. plain nonfat yogurt

1 t. no-salt Dijon mustard

Mix all ingredients. Serve on bed of lettuce, or on bread for a sandwich, if desired.
Prep. time: 20 min. *Serves 1.*

Chicken and Vegetable Especiál

For an elegant touch, add a little white wine.

4 chicken breasts, boned
and skinned (about 3
oz. each)

½ c. fresh parsley, diced

1 t. rosemary

2 cloves fresh garlic,
diced

½ t. pepper

2 large potatoes, sliced

1 c. peas

½ c. celery, diced
(include celery tops)

1 c. white wine

½ red onion, sliced

Per Serving		
Total Fat	3	gm
Saturated	0.8	gm
Unsaturated	2.2	gm
Cholesterol	65	mg
Sodium	116	mg
Carbohydrate	32	gm
Protein	30	gm
Fiber	5	gm
Calories	316	

Preheat oven to 375° F. Place chicken breasts on
bottom of deep, stainless steel, non-stick pan. Sprinkle
half parsley, rosemary, garlic, and pepper over chicken.
Place a layer of sliced potatoes across chicken. Sprinkle
½ c. of peas and ½ c. of celery over potatoes. Pour white
wine over mixture. Add another layer of potatoes and
peas. Add more wine if desired. Place onion slices over
mixture. Sprinkle with remaining rosemary, garlic,
and pepper. Cover with foil. Cook for 1 ½ to 2 hours.
Prep. time: 2 hours and 30 min. *Serves 4.*

*Note: For vegetarians, this dish can be made
without the chicken. Simply add an extra potato and an
extra ½ c. of peas to the recipe.*

Chicken Stew

1 broiler chicken, cut into parts

2 c. chopped tomatoes

4 large potatoes, peeled, cut into chunks

8 small white onions, peeled

4 carrots, scraped, cut into chunks

1 large green pepper, seeded, diced

2 stalks celery, cut into chunks

2 sprigs parsley

1 bay leaf

½ t. dried thyme

1 c. water

2 T. cornstarch

Place chicken pieces in a large pot. Add remaining ingredients, except cornstarch. Simmer, covered for 1 hour, or until chicken is tender. Spoon some of the hot liquid from the stew into the cornstarch (just enough to make a thin paste); stir well and then return all to the stew. Stir constantly over medium heat until gravy thickens. Remove chicken skin before serving.

Prep. time: 1 hour and 30 min. *Serves 4.*

Chicken Mexicana

¾ c. uncooked brown rice

1 tomato, peeled and diced

1 onion, finely diced

1 clove garlic, finely diced

1 T. olive oil

1 broiler chicken, cut up (about 2 ½ lb.)

2 c. water

½ t. chili powder

¼ t. pepper

In a non-stick skillet coated with nonfat cooking spray, brown the rice, stirring constantly. Add tomatoes, onion, and garlic. Cook and stir for several minutes. Add oil. Place chicken parts in a heavy saucepan. Add rice mixture, water, chili powder, and pepper. Bring to a boil. Lower heat, cover, and simmer about 25 min., until chicken and rice are tender. Serve with warm tortillas, if desired.

Prep. time: 50 min. *Serves 4.*

Chicken Paprikash

This is a beautiful dish for company. With its vibrant orange color, a deep green vegetable or a vegetable pasta would look perfect on the plate.

1 broiler chicken, cut into parts
2 t. sweet paprika
1 onion, thinly sliced
1 clove garlic, finely minced

1 c. Salt-Free Chicken Broth (see page 202)
1 T. olive oil
2 t. cornstarch
2 T. water

Per Serving		
Total Fat	17	gm
Saturated	4.1	gm
Unsaturated	12.9	gm
Cholesterol	161	mg
Sodium	139	mg
Carbohydrate	7	gm
Protein	54	gm
Fiber	1	gm
Calories	405	

Wash chicken parts and pat dry. Sprinkle with paprika on all sides. In a non-stick pan coated with nonfat cooking spray, sauté onion and garlic until limp. Push onion and garlic aside and sear chicken parts on all sides, continuously turning the pieces as you cook over medium heat. Add chicken broth and olive oil. Cover and cook over low heat for 1 hour. Combine cornstarch and water into a thin paste. Spoon some of the hot gravy into the paste, stir until smooth, then return to the skillet, stirring continuously. Cook and stir until gravy is thickened and transparent. Remove chicken skin before serving.
Prep. time: 1 hour and 30 min. *Serves 4.*

Oven-Fried Lemon Chicken

This is easy and different—tangy with a little hint of lemon.

½ c. nonfat lemon yogurt
½ t. ground ginger
½ t. garlic powder

8 broiler chicken thighs, skinned
½ c. whole wheat bread crumbs

Per Serving		
Total Fat	12	gm
Saturated	3.2	gm
Unsaturated	8.8	gm
Cholesterol	99	mg
Sodium	141	mg
Carbohydrate	5	gm
Protein	29	gm
Fiber	0.2	gm
Calories	250	

Preheat oven to 350° F. Mix yogurt, ginger, and garlic powder. Dip each chicken thigh into this mixture; then coat lightly with bread crumbs. Place coated thighs on a non-stick baking pan. Bake for 35 min., or until chicken is tender and coating is crisp.
Prep. time: 55 min. *Serves 4.*

Baked Spinach Balls

Per Serving

Total Fat	13	gm
Saturated	3.5	gm
Unsaturated	9.5	gm
Cholesterol	63	mg
Sodium	175	mg
Carbohydrate	19	gm
Protein	28	gm
Fiber	3	gm
Calories	316	

1 ½ lb. ground turkey
1 large onion, finely chopped
1 package (10 oz.) frozen spinach, thawed
1 egg white
¼ t. garlic powder
¼ t. pepper

1 can (16 oz.) unsalted tomato sauce
¼ c. dry red wine
1 c. Salt-Free Chicken Broth (see page 202)
1 T. cornstarch
2 T. water

Combine turkey, onion, spinach, egg white, garlic powder, and pepper. Mix well. Form into 1-inch balls. Place in heavy saucepan. Combine tomato sauce, wine, and chicken broth; pour over spinach balls. Cover tightly; cook over low heat 45 min. Stir cornstarch and water together to make a thin, lump-free paste; add several spoons of hot sauce from meatballs, then return all to saucepan, stirring constantly. Cook and stir until sauce thickens. Serve over hot cooked rice or noodles, if desired.
Prep. time: 1 hour and 15 min. *Serves 4.*

Poached Chicken Florentine

Per Serving

Total Fat	6	gm
Saturated	1.6	gm
Unsaturated	4.4	gm
Cholesterol	52	mg
Sodium	143	mg
Carbohydrate	10	gm
Protein	23	gm
Fiber	4	gm
Calories	181	

These spices give the chicken a very mellow flavor that's truly outstanding.

4 boneless, skinless chicken breast halves (about 1 lb.)
1 c. water
1 T. fresh lemon juice
1 sprig fresh dill weed
1 small onion, thinly sliced

1 carrot, scraped and grated
1 lb. fresh spinach, washed, trimmed
½ t. nutmeg
⅛ t. pepper

Preheat oven to 350° F. Arrange chicken breast halves in a large skillet. Pour water around chicken. Add lemon juice, dill weed, onion, and carrot. Cover and simmer gently for 20 minutes, or until chicken is cooked through. Remove chicken to a heated plate and reserve. Place washed spinach, nutmeg, and pepper into same skillet containing chicken cooking liquid. Cover and cook for several minutes, just until spinach is limp. Place poached chicken over spinach and rewarm for a minute or two. Serve chicken on a bed of cooked spinach.
Prep. time: 40 min. *Serves 4.*

Roast Chicken with Prune-Orange Stuffing

1 roaster chicken (about
   4 ½ lb.)

1 t. dried thyme

½ t. garlic powder

2 oranges

8 large pitted prunes

1 egg white

1 ½ c. dried bread cubes

Per Serving		
Total Fat	10	gm
Saturated	2.7	gm
Unsaturated	7.3	gm
Cholesterol	115	mg
Sodium	163	mg
Carbohydrate	21	gm
Protein	40	gm
Fiber	4	gm
Calories	336	

Preheat oven to 350° F. Rub chicken with thyme and
garlic powder, inside and outside. Chop pulp of
oranges and prunes; add egg white and bread cubes.
Mix well. If too dry, add a small amount of cool water
or orange juice to mixture. Stuff mixture into cavity of
chicken. Close cavity opening with skewers. Roast
chicken on a rack in a roasting pan for 2 hours, or
until tender. Baste occasionally with pan drippings.
Prep. time: 2 hours and 25 minutes. *Serves 8.*

Chicken Stroganoff

*This is an excellent low-fat version of the
original...who needs beef when you've got all the
flavor you could ever want?*

4 boneless, skinless
   chicken breast halves

¼ c. lemon juice

½ t. paprika

½ c. water

1 sprig fresh parsley

¼ c. plain nonfat yogurt

Per Serving		
Total Fat	8	gm
Saturated	2.3	gm
Unsaturated	5.7	gm
Cholesterol	83	mg
Sodium	80	mg
Carbohydrate	3	gm
Protein	31	gm
Fiber	0.1	gm
Calories	214	

Sprinkle chicken with lemon juice. Arrange chicken
in a non-stick skillet. Sprinkle with paprika. Add
water and parsley. Cover and simmer for 15 min.,
or until cooked through. Remove chicken to a warm
platter. Stir yogurt into cooking broth; cook and stir
over low heat to prevent curdling. Pour over chicken
and serve.
Prep. time: 35 min. *Serves 4.*

Sesame Chicken Kabobs

For a fun party idea, try using colorful toothpicks instead of skewers.

1 lb. boned and skinned chicken breasts

¾ c. orange juice

1 T. sesame seeds

1 T. brown sugar

2 t. grated orange peel

1 t. ground ginger

½ t. garlic powder

½ t. onion powder

⅛ t. ground red pepper

4 oz. fresh mushrooms, halved

1 green pepper, cut into 1-inch pieces

Pierce chicken with fork tines; cut into 1-inch pieces. In a small bowl, combine orange juice, sesame seeds, brown sugar, orange peel, ginger, garlic and onion powders, and red pepper. Add chicken, toss to coat, then marinate for 30 min. Preheat broiler to hot. Arrange chicken pieces on four 10-inch skewers, alternating with mushrooms and green peppers. Broil on a rack in a pan 3 to 4 inches from heat, until chicken is just cooked through, about 8 min. Brush frequently with marinade and turn chicken after 4 min. Prep. time: 1 hour and 10 min. *Serves 4.*

Broiled Turkey Cutlets Rosemary

4 turkey cutlets, about 1 lb.

½ c. apricot nectar

½ t. dried rosemary

¼ t. ginger

⅛ t. pepper

Arrange turkey cutlets on a broiling rack. Combine apricot nectar, rosemary, ginger, and pepper. Spoon half of mixture over cutlets. Broil 4 min. Turn cutlets and spoon remaining mixture over them. Broil 4 min. more, or until done to your taste. Prep. time: 20 min. *Serves 4.*

Turkey Balls Ratatouille

1 lb. raw ground turkey
1 small onion, grated
2 T. parsley, chopped
2 slices whole wheat
  bread
¾ c. water
1 can (6 oz.) salt-free
  tomato paste
1 clove garlic, minced
1 onion, thinly sliced

1 medium eggplant,
  peeled and diced into
  1-inch cubes
2 zucchini, sliced
1 green pepper, seeded
  and diced
4 tomatoes, chopped
¼ t. dried thyme
¼ t. dried oregano
⅛ t. pepper

Per Serving		
Total Fat	10	gm
Saturated	2.5	gm
Unsaturated	7.5	gm
Cholesterol	42	mg
Sodium	190	mg
Carbohydrate	40	gm
Protein	22	gm
Fiber	12	gm
Calories	325	

Combine ground turkey, onion, and parsley. Dip bread in water. Reserve water and shred bread over turkey mixture. Mix well. Form into 1-inch balls. Place in a large skillet. Combine tomato paste and reserved water; pour over turkey balls. Add garlic, onion, eggplant, zucchini, green pepper, tomatoes, thyme, oregano, and pepper. Cover and cook over low heat for 30 min.
Prep. time: 55 min. *Serves 4.*

Turkey-Oatmeal Loaf

1 lb. ground turkey
½ c. uncooked oatmeal
1 ripe banana, mashed
1 egg white

1 T. parsley, chopped
¼ t. pepper
¼ t. dried thyme

Per Serving		
Total Fat	6	gm
Saturated	1.6	gm
Unsaturated	4.4	gm
Cholesterol	28	mg
Sodium	44	mg
Carbohydrate	9	gm
Protein	12	gm
Fiber	1	gm
Calories	140	

Preheat oven to 350° F. Combine turkey, oatmeal, banana, and egg white until well blended. Add parsley, pepper, and thyme. Pack into 8 x 4-inch loaf pan. Bake for 1 hour.
Prep. time: 1 hour and 30 min. *Serves 6.*

Turkey-Tomato Sauce Loaf

Per Serving

Total Fat	6	gm
Saturated	1.8	gm
Unsaturated	4.2	gm
Cholesterol	29	mg
Sodium	75	mg
Carbohydrate	11	gm
Protein	13	gm
Fiber	1	gm
Calories	155	

1 lb. ground turkey
1 can (8 oz.) tomato sauce
½ c. uncooked oatmeal
1 egg white
1 small onion, grated
1 T. grated Parmesan cheese
1 T. parsley, chopped
½ t. garlic powder
¼ t. pepper

Preheat oven to 350° F. Combine turkey, ¼ c. tomato sauce, oatmeal, egg white, onion, cheese, parsley, garlic powder, and pepper. Mix well. Spoon into a non-stick loaf pan. Top with remaining tomato sauce. Bake for 1 hour.
Prep. time: 1 hour and 20 min. *Serves 6.*

Zesty Turkey Loaf

Per Serving

Total Fat	10	gm
Saturated	2.3	gm
Unsaturated	7.7	gm
Cholesterol	42	mg
Sodium	150	mg
Carbohydrate	9	gm
Protein	18	gm
Fiber	2	gm
Calories	198	

You'll get endless compliments on this dish because it seems so meaty.

2 lb. ground turkey, uncooked
3 slices rye or whole wheat bread, shredded
2 egg whites
1 onion, finely diced
2 t. prepared white horseradish
1 t. dry mustard
½ c. unsalted tomato sauce

Preheat oven to 375° F. Combine ground turkey with shredded bread. Add egg whites, onion, horseradish, and mustard. Add tomato sauce. Mix well, breaking down the bread bits as you go. Place in a 9 x 5-inch non-stick loaf pan. Bake for 1 ¼ hours.
Prep. time: 1 hour and 45 min. *Serves 8.*

Poached Fish

2 fillets of fish (4 oz. each)

1 clove garlic, halved

1 stalk celery, chopped

2 slices of lemon

Per Serving		
Total Fat	1	gm
Saturated	0.3	gm
Unsaturated	0.7	gm
Cholesterol	36	mg
Sodium	81	mg
Carbohydrate	1	gm
Protein	21	gm
Fiber	0.4	gm
Calories	105	

Preheat oven to 350° F. Place fish in baking pan that is not much bigger than the fish. Sprinkle on garlic, celery, and lemon. Add water to half cover fish, cover with foil, and bake for 20 min. Fish should be firm. Note: Red snapper was used in the nutritional analysis. You can use any mild fish.
Prep. time: 40 min. *Serves 2.*

Company Skillet Fish

1 T. minced green pepper

1 T. minced tomato

½ c. minced onion

1 clove garlic, minced

2 c. zucchini, cut into chunks

3 T. mild salsa

6 oz. red snapper (or similar low-fat fish), cut into chunks

1 ½ c. cooked brown rice

¼ c. water

Per Serving		
Total Fat	7	gm
Saturated	1.2	gm
Unsaturated	5.8	gm
Cholesterol	31	mg
Sodium	236	mg
Carbohydrate	46	gm
Protein	24	gm
Fiber	6	gm
Calories	342	

In a non-stick pan coated with nonfat cooking spray, sauté green pepper, tomato, onion, garlic, and zucchini chunks until green pepper is partially soft. Add salsa, fish chunks, brown rice, and water. Simmer over low heat for 15 to 20 min., until fish is thoroughly cooked.
Prep. time: 40 min. *Serves 2.*

Rolled Fillet of Sole

4 sole fillets (6 oz. each) ¼ t. curry powder

1 T. lemon juice ¼ c. chopped chives

¼ t. garlic powder 1 c. Mock Sour Cream

¼ t. mustard powder

¼ t. pepper

Preheat oven to 350° F. Spread both sides of fish with lemon juice. Sprinkle both sides with garlic powder, mustard powder, pepper, and curry powder. Mix chives with Mock Sour Cream (see recipe below) and spread ¼ of mixture on each fillet. Roll up fillets and fasten each with a toothpick. Bake for 20 min., or until fish is flaky.
Prep. time: 35 min. *Serves 4.*

Mock Sour Cream

½ can chilled evaporated 1 ½ T. plain nonfat yogurt
  skim milk

1 t. lemon juice

Combine milk with lemon juice until mixture thickens. Fold in yogurt.
Prep. time: 5 min. Makes 1 cup. *Serves 4.*

Breaded Crumb Fillet of Sole

4 sole fillets (6 oz. each)

2 T. lemon juice

1 chopped onion

3 stalks chopped celery

1 ½ c. water

1 c. sourdough bread crumbs, or matzo meal

1 T. parsley

Dash of paprika

Per Serving		
Total Fat	3	gm
Saturated	2.5	gm
Unsaturated	0.5	gm
Cholesterol	80	mg
Sodium	154	mg
Carbohydrate	33	gm
Protein	32	gm
Fiber	2	gm
Calories	289	

Preheat oven to 350° F. Spread both sides of fish with lemon juice and place in a non-stick baking dish. Sauté onion and celery in water and spoon over fillets. Mix bread crumbs or matzo meal with parsley. Crumble over fillets. Bake for 40 to 50 min. Garnish with paprika.

Prep. time: 1 hour and 15 min. *Serves 4.*

Herb-Stuffed Fillet of Sole

6 fillets of sole (about 1 ½ lb.)

2 t. prepared mustard

1 onion finely diced

¾ c. wheat germ

¼ c. fresh parsley, chopped

½ t. dried thyme

½ t. dried rosemary

⅛ t. pepper

Per Serving		
Total Fat	3	gm
Saturated	0.5	gm
Unsaturated	2.5	gm
Cholesterol	53	mg
Sodium	107	mg
Carbohydrate	11	gm
Protein	24	gm
Fiber	3	gm
Calories	247	

Preheat oven to 350° F. Place fillets flat. Cover surface with a thin coating of mustard. Combine remaining ingredients and sprinkle over mustard. Roll up fillets and fasten each with a toothpick. Place on a non-stick baking pan. Bake for 25 min., or until cooked through.

Prep. time: 50 min. *Serves 6.*

Sole Rolls with Vegetable Sauce

Per Serving

Total Fat	2	gm
Saturated	0.6	gm
Unsaturated	1.4	gm
Cholesterol	54	mg
Sodium	122	mg
Carbohydrate	13	gm
Protein	22	gm
Fiber	3	gm
Calories	164	

4 fillets of sole (about 1 lb.)

¼ c. lime juice

1 T. chopped chives

1 T. Parmesan cheese, grated

2 tomatoes, chopped

1 zucchini, thinly sliced

1 green pepper, finely diced

1 onion, finely diced

½ t. oregano

⅛ t. white pepper

¼ c. white wine or water

Lay fillets of sole flat. Sprinkle with lime juice, chopped chives, and grated Parmesan cheese. Roll up fillets and fasten each with a toothpick; set aside. In a large skillet, simmer tomatoes, zucchini, green pepper, onion, oregano, pepper, and wine for 3 min. Place prepared sole rolls in this mixture. Cover and cook over low heat for 5-7 min., or until fish flakes easily. Serve at once. Prep. time: 35 min. *Serves 4.*

Broiled Flounder Parmesan

Per Serving

Total Fat	2	gm
Saturated	0.6	gm
Unsaturated	1.4	gm
Cholesterol	54	mg
Sodium	117	mg
Carbohydrate	4	gm
Protein	20	gm
Fiber	1	gm
Calories	118	

1 lb. fillet of flounder

2 tomatoes, skinned, chopped

1 T. grated onion

¼ t. dried oregano

⅛ t. pepper

1 T. grated Parmesan cheese

Arrange flounder fillets on a broiling pan. Spoon chopped tomatoes over fish. Add grated onion, oregano, and pepper. Top with a sprinkling of Parmesan cheese. Broil 5-7 min., or until fish flakes easily.
Prep. time: 30 min. *Serves 4.*

Flounder Creole

2 c. tomatoes, chopped

1 can (8 oz.) tomato sauce

1 onion, finely diced

1 green pepper, finely diced

1 bay leaf

½ t. thyme

⅛ t. pepper

1 lb. flounder fillets

Per Serving		
Total Fat	2	gm
Saturated	0.5	gm
Unsaturated	1.5	gm
Cholesterol	77	mg
Sodium	470	mg
Carbohydrate	14	gm
Protein	30	gm
Fiber	3	gm
Calories	194	

Preheat oven to 375° F. Combine tomatoes, tomato sauce, onion, and green pepper in a saucepan. Add bay leaf, thyme, and pepper. Cook over low heat 15 min., stirring occasionally. Remove bay leaf. Arrange flounder fillets in a flat baking dish. Spoon sauce over fish. Bake for 20 min., or until fish flakes easily. Prep. time: 50 min. *Serves 4.*

Broiled Lemon-Flounder and Tomato

4 slices fillet of flounder (about 1 lb.)

1 lemon

½ t. dried dill weed

¼ t. paprika

2 tomatoes, halved through diameter

1 T. fresh parsley, chopped

2 T. whole grain bread crumbs

1 t. grated Parmesan cheese

Per Serving		
Total Fat	2	gm
Saturated	0.4	gm
Unsaturated	1.6	gm
Cholesterol	54	mg
Sodium	105	mg
Carbohydrate	4	gm
Protein	20	gm
Fiber	1	gm
Calories	113	

Place fish in a non-stick baking dish. Squeeze lemon over fish. Sprinkle with dill weed and paprika. Place halves of tomatoes, cut side up, in baking dish next to fish. Top tomato halves with parsley, bread crumbs, and a sprinkling of grated Parmesan cheese. Broil 7-8 min., or until fish flakes easily. Prep. time: 25 min. *Serves 4.*

Halibut Mousse

Per Serving

Total Fat	2	gm
Saturated	0.3	gm
Unsaturated	1.7	gm
Cholesterol	19	mg
Sodium	132	mg
Carbohydrate	7	gm
Protein	16	gm
Fiber	0.3	gm
Calories	112	

1 c. skim milk

2 c. bread crumbs

1 lb. raw halibut, ground
   or chopped fine

½ t. nutmeg

¼ t. white pepper

4 egg whites

Preheat oven to 350° F. Stir milk into bread crumbs. Add fish, nutmeg, and pepper. Beat egg whites separately until stiff; fold into fish mixture. Spoon mixture into a non-stick 8 x 4-inch loaf pan. Place this pan in a larger pan with 1 inch of hot water. Bake for 45 min., or until firm. Let stand 10 min. before slicing. Prep. time: 1 hour and 20 min. *Serves 8.*

Flounder with Broccoli Stuffing

Per Serving

Total Fat	2	gm
Saturated	0.4	gm
Unsaturated	1.6	gm
Cholesterol	53	mg
Sodium	108	mg
Carbohydrate	7	gm
Protein	21	gm
Fiber	2	gm
Calories	143	

1 small stalk broccoli

1 carrot, grated

⅛ t. ground nutmeg

⅛ t. pepper

2 fillets of flounder
   (about 4 oz. each)

1 T. lemon juice

¼ c. dry white wine

¼ t. paprika

Cut up broccoli; simmer in a small amount of water for several minutes until tender. Drain. Chop broccoli fine and add carrot, nutmeg, and pepper. Spread mixture over top of each piece of fish and roll up; fasten each fillet with a toothpick. Place rolled fillets in a small skillet or saucepan. Add lemon juice and white wine. Dust top of fish rolls with paprika. Cover and cook over medium heat for 5-7 min., or until fish flakes easily.
Prep. time: 30 min. *Serves 2.*

Baked Cod Oreganata

1 lb. cod fillets

1 clove garlic, finely minced

1 small onion, finely diced

½ green pepper, finely diced

3 tomatoes, chopped

½ t. oregano

⅛ t. pepper

½ c. dry white wine

Per Serving		
Total Fat	1	gm
Saturated	0.2	gm
Unsaturated	0.8	gm
Cholesterol	45	mg
Sodium	76	mg
Carbohydrate	10	gm
Protein	20	gm
Fiber	2	gm
Calories	148	

Preheat oven to 350° F. Arrange cod fillets in one layer in a flat, non-stick baking dish. Combine remaining ingredients, except wine. Spread mixture lightly over fish. Pour wine around fish. Bake, uncovered, for 25-30 min., or until fish flakes easily. Prep. time: 55 min. *Serves 4.*

Poached Salmon Veronique

2 thin, center slices fresh salmon

1 c. water

¼ c. cider vinegar

1 onion, sliced thin

1 sprig dill weed

3 whole cloves, chopped

1 bay leaf

1 peppercorn

½ c. seedless green grapes

2 lemon wedges

Per Serving		
Total Fat	5	gm
Saturated	0.9	gm
Unsaturated	4.1	gm
Cholesterol	20	mg
Sodium	706	mg
Carbohydrate	21	gm
Protein	18	gm
Fiber	3	gm
Calories	193	

Place salmon slices in a large skillet. Add water, vinegar, onion, dill weed, cloves, bay leaf, and peppercorn. Bring to a boil, then reduce heat and simmer, covered, 6 to 10 min., or until salmon is cooked through. Add grapes, cover and cook 1 minute more. Remove salmon from skillet with a slotted spatula. Serve garnished with grapes, lemon wedges, and additional sprigs of dill, if desired. Prep. time: 35 min. *Serves 2.*

Monkfish in Mushroom Cream Sauce

Per Serving

Total Fat	2	gm
Saturated	0.4	gm
Unsaturated	1.6	gm
Cholesterol	29	mg
Sodium	43	mg
Carbohydrate	7	gm
Protein	18	gm
Fiber	1	gm
Calories	137	

1 pound boneless monkfish

1 green pepper, seeded, chopped

½ c. sliced mushrooms

2 T. chopped chives

1 T. chopped fresh parsley

½ c. white wine or water

1 lemon

¼ c. evaporated skim milk

1 T. cornstarch

¼ t. paprika

Cut monkfish into 1-inch thick slices. Place fish in large non-stick skillet. Add green pepper, mushrooms, chives, parsley, wine, and juice of lemon. Cover; cook over low heat 5-7 min., or until fish is cooked through. Remove fish to a hot platter. Combine evaporated skim milk and cornstarch; mix until smooth. Stir into fish liquid. Cook and stir until liquid thickens. Pour over fish. Sprinkle with paprika. Serve at once.
Prep. time: 50 min. *Serves 4.*

Sautéed Oysters

Per Serving

Total Fat	2	gm
Saturated	0.5	gm
Unsaturated	1.5	gm
Cholesterol	46	mg
Sodium	100	mg
Carbohydrate	4	gm
Protein	6	gm
Fiber	0.3	gm
Calories	62	

1 pint fresh shelled oysters with juice

2 T. celery, finely chopped

2 T. green peppers, finely chopped

1 T. fresh parsley, finely chopped

2 t. lemon juice

¼ t. ground thyme

⅛ t. ground white pepper

Pour oysters and juice into a large non-stick skillet. Mix remaining ingredients and pour over oysters. Cook over low heat and stir until edges of oysters begin to curl, about 3 min. Serve over toast points, if desired.
Prep. time: 25 min. *Serves 4.*

Vegetables

Steamed Artichokes

Per Serving

Total Fat	0.2	gm
Saturated	0	gm
Unsaturated	0.2	gm
Cholesterol	0	mg
Sodium	469	mg
Carbohydrate	15	gm
Protein	4	gm
Fiber	4	gm
Calories	73	

This recipe is a healthy alternative to artichokes marinated in oil.

4 large artichokes   ¼ t. dill
1 bay leaf   ½ c. liquid Butter Buds
½ t. tarragon

Steam artichokes for approximately 45 min. in 1 inch of water that has been spiced with herbs. Serve with liquid Butter Buds for dipping.
Prep. time: 55 min. *Serves 4.*

Asparagus with Crumbles

Per Serving

Total Fat	2	gm
Saturated	0	gm
Unsaturated	2	gm
Cholesterol	0	mg
Sodium	242	mg
Carbohydrate	16	gm
Protein	6	gm
Fiber	6	gm
Calories	94	

6-8 stalks asparagus   ¼ t. Salt Sub
2 pieces whole wheat   (see page 235)
  bread   ¼ t. dry Butter Buds

Preheat oven to 400° F. Steam asparagus for 8 to 10 min., or just until tender. Cube bread and season with Salt Sub and dry Butter Buds. Toast seasoned bread cubes in oven on a non-stick cookie sheet. Crumble bread mixture over hot asparagus before serving.
Prep. time: 25 min. *Serves 1.*

Green Beans

Try not to overcook the green beans—the less they're cooked the greener they stay.

1 lb. green beans   1 t. basil

1 t. thyme   1 t. garlic powder

Per Serving		
Total Fat	0.2	gm
Saturated	0	gm
Unsaturated	0.2	gm
Cholesterol	0	mg
Sodium	15	mg
Carbohydrate	8	gm
Protein	2	gm
Fiber	0	gm
Calories	33	

Steam beans for 7 to 10 min. Mix thyme, basil, and garlic powder. Sprinkle mixture over beans.
Prep. time: 12 min. *Serves 4.*

Creole Green Beans

1 lb. green beans, trimmed

2 tomatoes, chopped

½ green pepper, finely diced

½ small onion, finely diced

1 okra pod, thinly sliced, optional

¼ c. water

⅛ t. thyme

⅛ t. pepper

Per Serving		
Total Fat	0.4	gm
Saturated	0.1	gm
Unsaturated	0.3	gm
Cholesterol	0	mg
Sodium	8	mg
Carbohydrate	12	gm
Protein	3	gm
Fiber	3	gm
Calories	51	

Wash green beans and place wet in a medium saucepan. Add remaining ingredients. Cover and cook over low heat until beans are tender, about 10 to 15 min.
Prep. time: 30 min. *Serves 6.*

Broccoli Polonaise

Per Serving

Total Fat	0.6	gm
Saturated	0.1	gm
Unsaturated	0.5	gm
Cholesterol	0	mg
Sodium	52	mg
Carbohydrate	10	gm
Protein	4	gm
Fiber	4	gm
Calories	52	

For this recipe, you can use either the whole stalk of broccoli or just the florets.

1 lb. fresh broccoli

½ c. fresh mushrooms, chopped

¼ c. salt-free tomato juice

1 T. fresh lemon juice

1 T. grated lemon rind

½ c. grated carrots

¼ c. bread crumbs

Trim broccoli and wash well. Drain. Cut the broccoli lengthwise, in half or in quarters, depending on thickness of stems. Steam in a small amount of water until tender. Drain. Meanwhile, in a small skillet, cook mushrooms in tomato juice until limp. Add remaining ingredients. Stir and heat through. Spoon over cooked broccoli and serve.
Prep. time: 25 min. *Serves 4.*

Cabbage Side Dish

Per Serving

Total Fat	6	gm
Saturated	0.8	gm
Unsaturated	5.2	gm
Cholesterol	0	mg
Sodium	29	mg
Carbohydrate	76	gm
Protein	6	gm
Fiber	10	gm
Calories	349	

4 c. shredded red or green cabbage

3 onions, chopped fine

2 lemons, juiced

4 Pippin apples, unpeeled and diced

¼ c. apple cider

3 T. honey

4 T. sesame seeds, ground until pasty

1 T. caraway seed

½ c. seedless raisins

⅛ t. ground allspice

Simmer all ingredients together in a covered saucepan for about 10 min.
Prep. time: 25 min. *Serves 6.*

Carrots Sesame

6 carrots, scrubbed and
  chopped

6 t. sesame seeds, hulled
  or unhulled

6 t. dry Butter Buds

Fresh parsley sprigs

Per Serving		
Total Fat	5	gm
Saturated	0.7	gm
Unsaturated	4.3	gm
Cholesterol	0	mg
Sodium	254	mg
Carbohydrate	25	gm
Protein	4	gm
Fiber	8	gm
Calories	151	

Steam carrots until "al dente" (until you can glide a fork into them easily). Combine sesame seeds with Butter Buds and sprinkle over hot carrots. Garnish with parsley.
Prep. time: 20 min. *Serves 2.*

Optional: Before garnishing carrots, you can broil them in the oven for 10 min. to brown. Garnish with parsley after removing from the oven.

Pickled Cucumbers

This makes a great side dish for summer picnics.

2 cucumbers, peeled,
  thinly sliced

1 onion, thinly sliced

1 c. water

¼ c. white vinegar

1 T. frozen apple juice
  concentrate

¼ t. white pepper

¼ t. dried dill weed

Per Serving		
Total Fat	0.2	gm
Saturated	0	gm
Unsaturated	0.2	gm
Cholesterol	0	mg
Sodium	6	mg
Carbohydrate	7	gm
Protein	1	gm
Fiber	1	gm
Calories	33	

Place sliced cucumbers and onion in a small deep bowl. Combine water, vinegar, apple juice concentrate, pepper, and dill weed; pour over cucumbers. Cover tightly and refrigerate for several hours or overnight. Stir occasionally.
Prep. time: 15 min. *Serves 6.*

Eggplant Parmesan

Per Serving

Total Fat	10	gm
Saturated	6.4	gm
Unsaturated	3.6	gm
Cholesterol	34	mg
Sodium	331	mg
Carbohydrate	8	gm
Protein	16	gm
Fiber	2	gm
Calories	183	

This makes a great main dish, especially for vegetarians.

1 can (16 oz.) salt-free tomatoes

2 T. salt-free tomato paste

1 t. dried oregano

1 eggplant, peeled and sliced thin

1 lb. sliced skim milk mozzarella cheese

¼ c. grated Parmesan cheese

Preheat oven to 350° F. Combine tomatoes, tomato paste, and oregano in an electric blender or food processor. Spoon some of the tomato mixture into a thin layer in a large flat baking dish. Cover with slices of eggplant laid side by side. Top with a layer of sliced mozzarella cheese. Sprinkle 1 T. of Parmesan cheese over all. Repeat a layer of sauce, eggplant, and cheese. Finish with a layer of eggplant, sauce, and remaining Parmesan cheese. Bake for 35 min., or until eggplant is fork-tender.
Prep. time: 1 hour and 15 min. *Serves 8.*

Stuffed Mushrooms

Per Serving

Total Fat	2	gm
Saturated	0.4	gm
Unsaturated	1.6	gm
Cholesterol	1	mg
Sodium	78	mg
Carbohydrate	8	gm
Protein	3	gm
Fiber	2	gm
Calories	54	

This is a popular appetizer to serve when you're entertaining guests.

4 T. unsalted spaghetti sauce

¼ green pepper

1 T. grated Parmesan cheese

1 slice whole wheat bread

8 oz. fresh mushrooms, stems removed

Preheat oven to 450° F. Blend all ingredients except mushrooms in a blender or food processor. Push the mixture down with a spoon when blender is off so it will blend smoothly. Stuff the mushroom cavities with this mixture. Place the mushrooms on a non-stick cookie sheet and bake for 15 min.
Prep. time: 35 min. *Serves 4.*

Stuffed Eggplant

A unique variation on stuffed peppers

2 medium eggplants

1 onion, diced

4 stalks celery, diced

1 c. salt-free tomato juice

½ t. oregano

1 egg white

1 c. raisin bran cereal

2 T. grated Parmesan cheese

Per Serving		
Total Fat	2	gm
Saturated	0.8	gm
Unsaturated	1.2	gm
Cholesterol	3	mg
Sodium	190	mg
Carbohydrate	34	gm
Protein	6	gm
Fiber	11	gm
Calories	160	

Preheat oven to 350° F. Cut eggplants in half lengthwise. Scoop out flesh, leaving unbroken shells. Dice scooped out eggplant flesh; place in a saucepan with onion, celery, tomato juice, and oregano. Simmer until vegetables are tender. Remove from heat. Add egg white and raisin bran to mixture in saucepan. Fill eggplant shells with this mixture. Sprinkle with grated Parmesan cheese. Bake for 20 min.
Prep. time: 50 min. *Serves 4.*

Baked Eggplant and Tomatoes

1 eggplant, about 2 lb.

½ lemon

½ t. oregano

⅛ t. pepper

4 medium tomatoes, chopped

2 oz. skim milk mozzarella cheese, diced

Per Serving		
Total Fat	2	gm
Saturated	0.8	gm
Unsaturated	1.2	gm
Cholesterol	4	mg
Sodium	41	mg
Carbohydrate	10	gm
Protein	3	gm
Fiber	4	gm
Calories	59	

Preheat oven to 375° F. Peel and cut eggplant in half lengthwise; slice into ¼-inch slices. Coat a non-stick skillet with nonfat cooking spray. In skillet, brown eggplant on both sides. Layer eggplant in a non-stick baking dish, seasoning with squirts of lemon juice, oregano, and pepper as you layer the slices. Place chopped tomatoes on top, then cover with diced cheese. Bake for 20 min., or until eggplant is tender.
Prep. time: 55 min. *Serves 8.*

Mushrooms Supreme

1 lb. fresh mushrooms, washed, dried

1 bunch minced scallions, or 1 medium Bermuda onion

1 red bell pepper, diced

4 medium tomatoes, diced

2 celery stalks, diced

1 T. vegetable broth seasoning

1 clove garlic, crushed

⅓ c. fresh parsley, minced

Juice of 1 large lemon

2 T. flax oil

1 t. fresh basil, optional

½ c. diced jicama, optional

Mix ingredients together. If desired, stir in basil and jicama. Chill.
Prep. time: 30 min. *Serves 4.*

Breaded Mushrooms

1 lb. fresh raw mushroom caps

4 beaten egg whites

4-6 crumbled whole grain bread slices

4 t. Salt Sub (see page 235)

Preheat oven to 350° F. Dip cleaned mushrooms into egg whites and place on a non-stick cookie sheet. Combine bread crumbs with Salt Sub and sprinkle over the mushrooms. Bake for 15 to 20 min., or until tender and crisp.
Prep. time: 40 min. *Serves 6.*

Baked Breaded Okra

Most people don't commonly prepare okra, but give this recipe a try. It's full of flavor.

1 lb. okra

1 medium onion, chopped

1 clove garlic, minced

1 c. unsalted tomato juice

1 t. oregano

4 crumbled whole grain bread slices

¼ c. Parmesan cheese, optional

Per Serving		
Total Fat	0.3	gm
Saturated	0.1	gm
Unsaturated	0.2	gm
Cholesterol	0	mg
Sodium	14	mg
Carbohydrate	16	gm
Protein	3	gm
Fiber	3	gm
Calories	73	

Preheat oven to 350° F. Mix everything but the bread. Place mixture in a non-stick baking dish and sprinkle with bread crumbs. Before baking, grate cheese over top, if desired. Bake for 45 min.
Prep. time: 60 min. *Serves 4.*

Potato-Carrot Pancakes

1 c. raw white potatoes, pared, shredded

1 c. raw carrots, shredded

1 small onion, finely chopped

½ c. skim milk

½ c. unbleached flour

2 egg whites, slightly beaten

½ t. dried dill weed

¼ t. pepper

Per Serving		
Total Fat	0.2	gm
Saturated	0.1	gm
Unsaturated	0.1	gm
Cholesterol	0.3	mg
Sodium	39	mg
Carbohydrate	20	gm
Protein	4	gm
Fiber	2	gm
Calories	101	

Combine potatoes, carrots, and onion in a bowl. Add milk and flour. Stir in egg whites, dill weed, and pepper. Mix well. If mixture is too thin, add another tablespoon or two of flour. Drop by tablespoon onto a non-stick griddle. Brown on one side, turn, and brown on other side.
Prep. time: 50 min. *Serves 6.*

Mashed Potato Puff

Per Serving

Total Fat	0.3 gm
Saturated	0.1 gm
Unsaturated	0 gm
Cholesterol	0.2 mg
Sodium	38 mg
Carbohydrate	44 gm
Protein	7 gm
Fiber	4 gm
Calories	199

6 potatoes, peeled and quartered

1 small onion, sliced

½ t. dried dill weed

¼ c. skim milk

2 egg whites

⅛ t. ground white pepper

⅛ t. paprika

Preheat oven to 350° F. Place potatoes, onion, and dill weed in a heavy saucepan. Add an inch of water, cover, and cook until potatoes are tender, about 20 min. Drain, reserving liquid. Mash potatoes and onion, add skim milk to soften mixture. Beat egg whites until stiff peaks form; fold through potato mixture until well blended. Add pepper. Spoon mixture into non-stick casserole dish. Swirl top with a fork. Sprinkle with paprika. Bake 20 min. Prep. time: 1 hour and 20 min. *Serves 6.*

Twice-Baked Potatoes

Per Serving

Total Fat	2 gm
Saturated	0.5 gm
Unsaturated	1.5 gm
Cholesterol	1 mg
Sodium	154 mg
Carbohydrate	35 gm
Protein	6 gm
Fiber	4 gm
Calories	179

4 baking potatoes

2 egg whites

2 T. Butter Buds

1 T. Parmesan cheese

1 T. onion, finely chopped

1 t. olive oil

1 t. crushed, dried thyme

⅛ t. pepper

½ t. paprika

Preheat oven to 350° F. Bake potatoes for 40 min. Slice off ½ inch lengthwise from each potato. Scoop out the pulp and place in a mixing bowl. Reserve the shells. Beat the potato pulp with all remaining ingredients, except paprika. Return mixture to shells; sprinkle with paprika, and bake for 15 min. Prep. time: 1 hour and 20 min. *Serves 4.*

Carrot-Stuffed Baked Potato

2 baking potatoes
½ c. skim milk
2 soft-cooked carrots

¼ t. dill weed
2 T. grated Parmesan cheese

Per Serving		
Total Fat	0.2	gm
Saturated	0.2	gm
Unsaturated	0	gm
Cholesterol	1	mg
Sodium	46	mg
Carbohydrate	22	gm
Protein	4	gm
Fiber	3	gm
Calories	105	

Preheat oven to 350° F. Scrub potatoes and bake 1 hour. Remove from oven. Cut potatoes in half the long way. Scoop out cooked potato, reserving skin shells. Mash with milk, carrots, and dill weed. Spoon mixture back into reserved potato shells. Top with grated cheese. Return to oven to melt cheese and heat through.
Prep. time: 1 hour and 20 min. *Serves 4.*

Pink Potatoes and Peas

This is a very elegant side dish that goes well with either a chicken or fillet of fish entrée.

4 small red new potatoes (approximately 3 inches long)
½ c. water

2 c. peas
½ c. chopped onion
1 t. olive oil
½ t. sweet basil

Per Serving		
Total Fat	2	gm
Saturated	0.2	gm
Unsaturated	1.8	gm
Cholesterol	0	mg
Sodium	79	mg
Carbohydrate	36	gm
Protein	7	gm
Fiber	5	gm
Calories	180	

Preheat oven to 350° F. Peel a small strip around the center of each potato. In a 1-quart casserole with a cover, place the water, peas, and onion. Nestle the potatoes on top, drizzle with olive oil, and sprinkle with basil. Cover and bake for 40 min.
Prep. time 60 min. *Serves 4.*

Bavarian Potatoes

Per Serving

Total Fat	40	gm
Saturated	0.5	gm
Unsaturated	39.5	gm
Cholesterol	120	mg
Sodium	669	mg
Carbohydrate	62	gm
Protein	39	gm
Fiber	5	gm
Calories	755	

4 c. hot mashed potatoes

3 c. crumbled hoop cheese or farmer cheese

¾ c. plain nonfat yogurt

½ onion, finely chopped

1 ½ t. Salt Sub (see page 235)

1 T. Butter Buds

¼ c. slivered almonds

¼ c. bread crumbs

⅛ t. paprika

Preheat oven to 350° F. Mix the first 5 ingredients. Pour into a non-stick baking dish. Brush top with liquid Butter Buds. Top with almonds and bread crumbs; sprinkle with paprika. Bake for 30 to 40 min. Prep. time: 1 hour and 20 min. *Serves 4.*

Spinach Cheese Soufflé

Per Serving

Total Fat	1	gm
Saturated	0.3	gm
Unsaturated	0.7	gm
Cholesterol	1	mg
Sodium	197	mg
Carbohydrate	4	gm
Protein	7	gm
Fiber	3	gm
Calories	46	

1 package (10 oz.) frozen chopped spinach

½ c. 1% low-fat cottage cheese

1 scallion including top, thinly sliced

¼ t. nutmeg

⅛ t. white pepper

2 egg whites

Preheat oven to 350° F. Cook spinach in a small amount of water and drain well. Add cottage cheese, scallion, nutmeg, and pepper. Beat egg whites until stiff peaks form; fold through spinach mixture. Pour into a non-stick baking dish. Bake for 20 min., or until firm.
Prep. time: 1 hour. *Serves 4.*

Creamed Spinach

This dish can even be used as a dip served with tortilla chips.

1 lb. fresh spinach

1 small onion, grated

¼ t. nutmeg

⅛ t. pepper

½ c. plain nonfat yogurt

Per Serving		
Total Fat	1	gm
Saturated	0.1	gm
Unsaturated	0.9	gm
Cholesterol	1	mg
Sodium	111	mg
Carbohydrate	10	gm
Protein	5	gm
Fiber	4	gm
Calories	56	

Wash spinach leaves and trim off roots and stems. Place in a skillet with a small amount of water. Add onion, nutmeg, and pepper. Cook, covered, over low heat, until tender, about 5 min. Drain well. Toss with yogurt and serve.
Prep. time: 20 min. *Serves 4.*

Quick Creamed Spinach

1 package (10 oz.) frozen spinach, thawed

¼ c. plain nonfat yogurt

½ t. onion powder

¼ t. nutmeg

Per Serving		
Total Fat	0.4	gm
Saturated	0.1	gm
Unsaturated	0.3	gm
Cholesterol	1	mg
Sodium	142	mg
Carbohydrate	10	gm
Protein	6	gm
Fiber	3	gm
Calories	58	

Cook spinach. Drain. Blend yogurt with onion powder and nutmeg. Stir seasoned yogurt into spinach. Serve immediately.
Prep. time: 15 min. *Serves 2.*

Yolkless Spinach Frittata

Per Serving

Total Fat	4	gm
Saturated	0.7	gm
Unsaturated	3.3	gm
Cholesterol	1	mg
Sodium	118	mg
Carbohydrate	9	gm
Protein	7	gm
Fiber	1	gm
Calories	95	

½ lb. fresh trimmed spinach, or 1 package (10 oz.) frozen spinach

½ lb. fresh mushrooms, sliced

1 small onion, diced fine

4 egg whites

⅛ t. pepper

⅛ t. dried dill weed

1 T. olive oil

2 t. grated Parmesan cheese

Cook spinach in a small amount of water. Drain well. In a large skillet coated with nonfat cooking spray, sauté mushrooms and onions until limp. Beat egg whites until soft peaks form. Stir in drained spinach, pepper, and dill weed; mix well. Pour mixture over mushrooms and onions in the skillet. Cook over medium heat until mixture is set. Remove from heat and add oil. Sprinkle with grated Parmesan cheese. Broil until cheese melts and top is lightly browned. Cut into wedges and serve at once.
Prep. time: 45 min. *Serves 4.*

Spaghetti Squash

Per Serving

Total Fat	11	gm
Saturated	1.8	gm
Unsaturated	9.2	gm
Cholesterol	2	mg
Sodium	81	mg
Carbohydrate	32	gm
Protein	7	gm
Fiber	10	gm
Calories	246	

1 small spaghetti squash (4 c. when cooked)

1 ½ c. unsalted spaghetti sauce

¼ c. water

1 ½ T. vegetable broth seasoning

2 t. grated Parmesan cheese

Cut squash in half, scoop out seeds, and place cut side down in a pot with 1 inch of water. Cover pot and steam squash for 20 min. Remove from water and scoop out the strands with a fork. Combine spaghetti sauce with water and vegetable broth seasoning. Top squash strands with the sauce; sprinkle with Parmesan cheese.
Prep. time: 40 min. *Serves 2.*

Winter Squash

A slightly sweet and very tasty treat!

1 acorn, butternut, or
  banana squash
4 T. liquid Butter Buds

1 T. honey
1 t. nutmeg
1 t. cinnamon

Per Serving		
Total Fat	1	gm
Saturated	0.4	gm
Unsaturated	0.6	gm
Cholesterol	0	mg
Sodium	373	mg
Carbohydrate	69	gm
Protein	5	gm
Fiber	8	gm
Calories	275	

Preheat oven to 300° F. Cut squash in half
lengthwise; remove and discard the seeds. Place
in an uncovered non-stick baking dish with the
insides up. Brush with a mixture of Butter Buds,
honey, nutmeg, and cinnamon. Bake for 1 hour.
Prep. time: 1 hour and 15 min. *Serves 2.*

Baked Stuffed Butternut Squash

2 small butternut squash
½ c. grated carrots
¼ c. white seedless raisins
¼ c. frozen apple juice
  concentrate

⅛ t. ginger
⅛ t. nutmeg

Per Serving		
Total Fat	0.3	gm
Saturated	0.1	gm
Unsaturated	0.2	gm
Cholesterol	0	mg
Sodium	15	mg
Carbohydrate	28	gm
Protein	2	gm
Fiber	3	gm
Calories	108	

Preheat oven to 350° F. Cut squash in half
lengthwise; remove and discard seeds. Combine
carrots, raisins, apple juice concentrate, ginger, and
nutmeg. Stuff squash cavities with this mixture.
Place squash halves in a baking pan. Bake in an
uncovered non-stick baking dish for 40 min., or until
fork-tender.
Prep. time: 55 min. *Serves 4.*

Zuccatash

Per Serving

Total Fat	2	gm
Saturated	0.2	gm
Unsaturated	1.8	gm
Cholesterol	0	mg
Sodium	25	mg
Carbohydrate	16	gm
Protein	4	gm
Fiber	3	gm
Calories	90	

1 medium zucchini (approximately 1 ½ c., cut up) sliced and quartered

1 package (10 oz.) frozen corn and lima beans

1 c. water

1 t. olive oil

1 rounded t. tomato paste

2 t. vegetable broth seasoning

Cook all ingredients together in a small pot until the zucchini is tender, about 12 min.
Prep. time: 25 min. *Serves 4.*

Tomatoes Vinaigrette

Per Serving

Total Fat	4	gm
Saturated	0.5	gm
Unsaturated	3.5	gm
Cholesterol	0	mg
Sodium	10	mg
Carbohydrate	6	gm
Protein	1	gm
Fiber	1	gm
Calories	55	

Delicious, especially in the summer, when ripe cherry tomatoes are plentiful.

2 T. flax or olive oil

2 T. red wine vinegar

2 T. fresh lemon juice

1 clove garlic, crushed

½ t. dried basil

½ t. dried thyme

1 t. fresh parsley, chopped

⅛ t. ground white pepper

2 pints cherry tomatoes, stems removed

To make vinaigrette, combine all ingredients, except tomatoes. Mix well. Place tomatoes in a bowl and pour vinaigrette over all. Toss lightly to coat well. Chill for several hours before serving.
Prep. time: 15 min. *Serves 8.*

Yam Bake

Don't limit yams to your Thanksgiving dinner.
They're delicious all year 'round.

2 small yams, peeled and
cut into "carrot stick"
pieces

1 T. olive oil

1 T. Parmesan cheese,
grated

1 small onion, chopped

Per Serving		
Total Fat	8	gm
Saturated	1.6	gm
Unsaturated	6.4	gm
Cholesterol	3	mg
Sodium	79	mg
Carbohydrate	69	gm
Protein	6	gm
Fiber	1	gm
Calories	364	

Preheat oven to 350° F. Toss all ingredients together
and put into a 1-quart casserole dish. Cover and bake
for 1 hour, removing the casserole lid the last 15
min. Serve hot.
Prep. time: 1 hour and 25 min. *Serves 2.*

Cabbage and Potatoes

3 c. potatoes, diced

1 medium onion,
chopped

½ head green cabbage,
chopped

2 stalks celery, chopped

2 carrots, sliced

¼ t. fennel

¼ t. caraway seeds

Per Serving		
Total Fat	1	gm
Saturated	0.1	gm
Unsaturated	0.9	gm
Cholesterol	0	mg
Sodium	57	mg
Carbohydrate	44	gm
Protein	6	gm
Fiber	7	gm
Calories	196	

Place all ingredients, except fennel and caraway
seeds, into a pot with a small amount of water.
Steam for 10 min. Add fennel and caraway seeds.
Cook 10 more min.
Prep. time: 35 min. *Serves 4.*

Soups

Salt-Free Chicken Broth

Per Serving

Total Fat	6	gm
Saturated	1.6	gm
Unsaturated	4.4	gm
Cholesterol	69	mg
Sodium	92	mg
Carbohydrate	15	gm
Protein	24	gm
Fiber	4	gm
Calories	208	

This is an excellent base for many soups. Use it on its own, or add noodles and vegetables.

1 whole chicken, about 3 lb.

2 quarts water

1 large onion, peeled

4 carrots, scraped

2 stalks celery with leaves

2 parsnips, scraped

1 sprig parsley

1 sprig dill weed

¼ t. ground white pepper

¼ t. thyme

1 bay leaf

Wash and clean chicken; place in a heavy pot with lid. Add remaining ingredients. Simmer 1 ½ hours. Remove chicken. Strain broth through a fine sieve. Discard celery, parsley, dill weed, and onion. Slice carrots and parsnips; return to soup. Remove chicken from bones and add to soup. Chill soup to allow fat to solidify on top, then remove fat and discard before reheating soup.
Prep. time: 2 hours and 30 min. *Serves 8.*

Good and Green Soup

Per Serving

Total Fat	1	gm
Saturated	0.1	gm
Unsaturated	0.9	gm
Cholesterol	0	mg
Sodium	21	mg
Carbohydrate	22	gm
Protein	4	gm
Fiber	5	gm
Calories	97	

4 medium-sized zucchini, sliced

2 leeks, sliced

1 potato, diced

4 ¼ c. water

1 t. garlic powder

1 t. chives

1 t. parsley flakes

Lightly steam zucchini, leeks, and potato with ¼ c. water. Add remaining water to steamed vegetables; mash lightly. Add seasonings, heat and serve.
Prep. time: 45 min. *Serves 4.*

Tomato Bouillon Soup

For tomato lovers only—and you'll love it!

4 tomatoes

5 ½ c. tomato juice

¼ chili pepper, chopped

2 T. chopped parsley

¼ t. oregano

¼ t. garlic

¼ t. dill seed

¼ t. ground cloves

1 bay leaf

Per Serving		
Total Fat	0.4	gm
Saturated	0	gm
Unsaturated	0.4	gm
Cholesterol	0	mg
Sodium	23	mg
Carbohydrate	11	gm
Protein	2	gm
Fiber	3	gm
Calories	44	

Purée tomatoes in a blender. Place puréed tomatoes and remaining ingredients in a large pot. Bring to a boil; simmer for ½ hour.
Prep. time: 50 min. *Serves 6.*

Garden Soup

5 c. water

1 potato, scrubbed and diced

1 carrot, scrubbed and diced

1 small tomato, diced

1 small yellow onion, diced

1 c. cabbage, chopped

½ c. cooked garbanzo beans

1 c. peas, fresh or frozen, thawed

1 apple, peeled and diced

4 oz. vegetable rotelli (spiral pasta)

1 T. olive oil

⅛ t. pepper

1 T. vegetable broth seasoning

Per Serving		
Total Fat	4	gm
Saturated	0.6	gm
Unsaturated	3.4	gm
Cholesterol	0	mg
Sodium	93	mg
Carbohydrate	47	gm
Protein	7	gm
Fiber	6	gm
Calories	249	

Start water boiling as you prepare vegetables. Add vegetables to pot one by one as they are ready. Add pasta, cover, and cook for 10 min. Add oil and seasonings; simmer 3 to 5 more min.
Prep. time: 45 min. *Serves 4.*

Barley-Bean Soup

Per Serving

Total Fat	0.2	gm
Saturated	0	gm
Unsaturated	0.2	gm
Cholesterol	0	mg
Sodium	14	mg
Carbohydrate	34	gm
Protein	4	gm
Fiber	4	gm
Calories	142	

You can feel especially good when you eat beans. Not only are they richly satisfying, their protein, unlike meat protein, has none of the uric acid that contributes to gout.

1 c. Great Northern dried beans

½ c. barley

1 onion, sliced thin

2 carrots, scraped and sliced

2 stalks celery, sliced

2 parsnips, scraped and sliced

1 turnip, peeled, and cut into chunks

2 cloves garlic, minced

2 sprigs dill weed

1 sprig parsley

1 t. dried basil

½ t. pepper

Soak beans for 1 hour. Pour off water. Add remaining ingredients and cover with 2 quarts water. Cover and cook over low heat for 3 hours, or until beans are tender. Stir occasionally.
Prep. time: 4 hours and 30 min. *Serves 10.*

Corn Chowder

Per Serving

Total Fat	1	gm
Saturated	0.1	gm
Unsaturated	0.9	gm
Cholesterol	0	mg
Sodium	29	mg
Carbohydrate	30	gm
Protein	6	gm
Fiber	5	gm
Calories	145	

The leeks give this wonderful flavor.

1 ½ c. potatoes, cubed

1 T. carrots, diced

¼ c. leek, chopped

3 c. water

1 ⅔ c. corn

1 t. vegetable broth seasoning

2 sprigs parsley

Simmer potatoes, carrots, and leek in water until tender. Remove some of liquid from pot. Use this liquid to blend the corn. Add blended corn and vegetable broth seasoning to pot. Bring to boiling point. Garnish with parsley.
Prep. time: 50 min. *Serves 2.*

Black Bean Soup

1 lb. dried black beans

2 quarts water

6 cloves garlic, diced

2 onions, diced

6 sweet chili peppers,
seeded and chopped

2 T. olive oil

¼ t. pepper

¼ t. dried oregano

¼ t. ground cumin

2 bay leaves

1 ½ T. vinegar

1 T. frozen apple juice
concentrate

Per Serving		
Total Fat	4	gm
Saturated	0.6	gm
Unsaturated	3.4	gm
Cholesterol	0	mg
Sodium	14	mg
Carbohydrate	42	gm
Protein	13	gm
Fiber	5	gm
Calories	248	

Wash beans well, discarding any shriveled ones. Soak overnight. Drain, rinse in fresh water, and drain again. Place in a large heavy pot with 2 quarts water. Bring to boil, reduce heat, cover, and cook 45 min. Sauté garlic, onions, and chili peppers for 10 min. in a non-stick skillet coated with nonfat cooking spray, stirring occasionally. Add 1 c. of drained cooked black beans, Mash together and pour into pot with cooked beans. Add oil, pepper, oregano, cumin, and bay leaves. Mix well, cover, and cook over low heat for 1 hour. Add vinegar and apple juice concentrate. Serve with additional chopped onion on top, if desired.
Prep. time: 2 hours and 25 min., plus soaking time.
Serves 8.

Lentil Soup

Lentils are considered the "King of Beans," because they are more digestible, more alkaline, and more easily cooked than any other bean.

1 ½ c. water

½ c. dry lentils

1 sliced carrot

1 t. Salt Sub
(see page 235)

⅛ t. basil

¼ t. parsley

Per Serving		
Total Fat	0.4	gm
Saturated	0.1	gm
Unsaturated	0.3	gm
Cholesterol	0	mg
Sodium	213	mg
Carbohydrate	20	gm
Protein	8	gm
Fiber	2	gm
Calories	111	

Simmer all ingredients about 20 to 25 min., or until lentils are tender (water will be absorbed, vegetables will be soupy).
Prep. time: 40 min. *Serves 2.*

Traditional Split-Pea Soup

Per Serving

Total Fat	2	gm
Saturated	0.8	gm
Unsaturated	1.2	gm
Cholesterol	0.4	mg
Sodium	164	mg
Carbohydrate	99	gm
Protein	23	gm
Fiber	7	gm
Calories	500	

1 ½ c. uncooked split peas

8 c. water

1 c. apple juice

1 c. chopped carrot (approximately 3 carrots)

½ c. salsa

1 c. chopped yellow onion

1 c. uncooked rice

3 T. vegetable broth seasoning

1 T. tomato paste

Soak peas overnight. Cook all ingredients together in a pot, watching to make sure it does not boil over, until the peas are tender and the rice is done (at least 1 hour).
Prep. time: 1 hour and 40 min., plus soaking time.
Serves 4.

Curried Split-Pea Soup

Per Serving

Total Fat	0.3	gm
Saturated	0	gm
Unsaturated	0.3	gm
Cholesterol	0	mg
Sodium	13	mg
Carbohydrate	18	gm
Protein	5	gm
Fiber	4	gm
Calories	88	

If you want this to be spicier, just add more curry powder.

2 c. dried split peas

2 ½ quarts water

1 large carrot, grated

2 medium potatoes, grated

1 large onion, grated

1 t. curry powder

¼ t. pepper

Wash split peas, drain, and place in a large kettle with a tight-fitting lid. Add water, carrot, potatoes, onion, curry powder, and pepper. Cover and bring to a boil; then lower heat and simmer for about 2 hours, or until peas are soft. Stir until peas fall apart, or press soup through a strainer.
Prep. time: 2 hours and 20 min. *Serves 10.*

Lima-Barley Soup

This soup takes time, but it's worth the wait.

1 c. dried small lima beans

½ c. barley

2 c. chopped tomatoes

4 carrots, scraped and sliced

4 stalks celery, thinly sliced

2 onions, thinly sliced

1 clove garlic, finely minced

1 bay leaf

2 whole cloves

1 T. lemon juice

¼ t. pepper

2 quarts water

Per Serving		
Total Fat	1	gm
Saturated	0.1	gm
Unsaturated	0.9	gm
Cholesterol	0	mg
Sodium	32	mg
Carbohydrate	28	gm
Protein	7	gm
Fiber	5	gm
Calories	140	

In a heavy soup pot, soak beans covered with water for several hours, or overnight. Drain. Add remaining ingredients and 2 quarts fresh water. Bring to a boil, reduce heat, cover and simmer 3 hours, or until beans are tender.
Prep. time: 3 hours and 30 min., plus soaking time.
Serves 10.

Cabbage-Bean Soup

Cabbage belongs to the family of crucifers, which has been shown to have cancer-inhibiting compounds.

1 c. cooked navy beans

¼ c. chopped onions

1 stalk celery, sliced

3 raw potatoes, diced

6 c. shredded cabbage (approximately 1 lb.)

3 c. water

½ t. crushed bay leaf

4 T. vegetable broth seasoning

2 c. puréed tomatoes

Per Serving		
Total Fat	3	gm
Saturated	0.1	gm
Unsaturated	2.9	gm
Cholesterol	0	mg
Sodium	371	mg
Carbohydrate	51	gm
Protein	12	gm
Fiber	8	gm
Calories	265	

Combine all ingredients and simmer in covered pot for about 20 min., or until diced potatoes are tender.
Prep. time: 45 min. *Serves 4.*

Black-Eyed Pea Soup

Per Serving

Total Fat	5	gm
Saturated	0.7	gm
Unsaturated	4.3	gm
Cholesterol	0	mg
Sodium	49	mg
Carbohydrate	36	gm
Protein	4	gm
Fiber	10	gm
Calories	217	

4 c. water

1 c. celery, chopped

2 c. cabbage, chopped

4 rounded T. orzo (rice-like pasta)

1 medium zucchini, quartered and sliced

½ c. cooked baby lima beans

¼ c. cooked kidney beans

½ c. cooked barley

1 c. cooked black-eyed peas

¼ c. unsalted spaghetti sauce

1 T. vegetable broth seasoning

1 T. olive oil

Put water in large pot; add celery, cabbage, orzo, zucchini, lima beans, kidney beans, barley, and black-eyed peas. Cook for 20 min. Add spaghetti sauce and seasoning; cook 10 min. more. Stir in olive oil and serve.

Prep. time: 1 hour. *Serves 4.*

Cauliflower Soup

Per Serving

Total Fat	4	gm
Saturated	0.5	gm
Unsaturated	3.5	gm
Cholesterol	2	mg
Sodium	91	mg
Carbohydrate	36	gm
Protein	9	gm
Fiber	11	gm
Calories	203	

We've found that even people who don't love vegetables develop a whole new respect for them with soups like this one.

5 c. water

1 small head cauliflower, cut up

½ c. corn

1 c. lima beans

1 small zucchini, sliced and quartered

3 T. spinach pastina

1 ½ c. cooked barley

4 rounded T. unsalted spaghetti sauce

1 ½ T. vegetable broth seasoning

2 t. olive oil

In a medium or large pot, bring all ingredients except oil to a boil. Simmer for 20 min. Stir in oil.

Prep. time: 50 min. *Serves 4.*

Minestrone Soup

Great taste is the biggest thing this hearty, traditional soup has going for it.

¾ c. sliced carrot

¾ c. sliced celery

¼ c. chopped onion

¾ c. green beans

½ c. whole grain
   macaroni

1 c. sliced zucchini

1 quart water

1 ½ c. tomato purée

¾ c. cooked kidney beans

1 ½ T. chopped parsley

2 ½ T. chopped scallion

1 t. basil

4 T. vegetable broth
   seasoning

Per Serving		
Total Fat	3	gm
Saturated	0.1	gm
Unsaturated	2.4	gm
Cholesterol	0	mg
Sodium	61	mg
Carbohydrate	41	gm
Protein	11	gm
Fiber	7	gm
Calories	226	

Simmer all ingredients together until the carrots are tender.

Prep. time: 50 min. *Serves 4.*

Alphabet Soup

Fun to make, and much better for everyone than the canned choices.

4 c. water

1 package (20 oz.)
   "Italian Vegetables"
   (zucchini, cauliflower,
   carrots, Italian green
   beans, lima beans), or
   an equivalent mixture

½ c. uncooked alphabet
   macaroni (2.6 oz.)

4 T. unsalted spaghetti
   sauce

2 T. vegetable broth
   seasoning

Per Serving		
Total Fat	3	gm
Saturated	0.4	gm
Unsaturated	2.6	gm
Cholesterol	0	mg
Sodium	119	mg
Carbohydrate	66	gm
Protein	13	gm
Fiber	1	gm
Calories	326	

Combine all ingredients in a medium or large pot; simmer for 20 min.

Prep. time: 40 min. *Serves 2.*

Cabbage-Mac Soup

Per Serving		
Total Fat	5	gm
Saturated	0.7	gm
Unsaturated	4.3	gm
Cholesterol	0	mg
Sodium	87	mg
Carbohydrate	32	gm
Protein	6	gm
Fiber	5	gm
Calories	191	

8 c. water

½ Spanish onion

1 small zucchini, sliced and quartered

1 c. elbow macaroni (whole wheat, if you wish)

½ small head cabbage, chopped coarsely

4 or 5 small end slices of eggplant (no seeds)

1 c. canned garbanzo beans, rinsed

3 T. unsalted spaghetti sauce

2 T. vegetable broth seasoning

1 T. olive oil

Pour water into a large pot, then add remaining ingredients, except oil. Simmer until macaroni is tender, about 20 min. Stir in oil and serve.
Prep. time: 1 hour. *Serves 4.*

Spinach-Spaghetti Soup

Per Serving		
Total Fat	2	gm
Saturated	0.2	gm
Unsaturated	1.8	gm
Cholesterol	0	mg
Sodium	65	mg
Carbohydrate	28	gm
Protein	6	gm
Fiber	7	gm
Calories	142	

Greens and pasta are a favorite in Italy. This recipe came from an Italian gentleman who passed through the Institute years ago.

7 ½ c. water

2 oz. spinach spaghetti

½ onion, chopped

½ medium green pepper, chopped fine

1 head broccoli (remove center stem and use only florets and tender stems)

1 c. cooked barley

½ c. cooked garbanzo beans

3 T. vegetable broth seasoning

3 T. unsalted spaghetti sauce

Boil water in a large pot; add spinach spaghetti, onion, green pepper, broccoli, barley, and beans. Let simmer 20 min., then add remaining ingredients and cook 10 min. longer.
Prep. time: 1 hour. *Serves 4.*

Mineghetti Soup

6 c. water

1 c. zucchini chunks
(1 small zucchini)

½ c. diced red onion
(¼ medium onion)

1 ½ c. eggplant chunks
(¼ small eggplant)

2 oz. spaghetti, broken

1 ½ c. diced yellow
squash (2 small
squash)

½ c. chopped celery
(1 stalk)

½ c. cooked mushrooms

1 c. cooked kidney beans

1 c. frozen peas

5 heaping T. unsalted
spaghetti sauce

2 T. vegetable broth
seasoning

Per Serving		
Total Fat	3	gm
Saturated	0.3	gm
Unsaturated	2.7	gm
Cholesterol	0	mg
Sodium	31	mg
Carbohydrate	35	gm
Protein	9	gm
Fiber	6	gm
Calories	199	

Combine all ingredients in a large pot in the order
listed. Begin cooking while you prepare ingredients,
adding them as they are ready. Simmer until vegetables
are tender (20 min. minimum, once spaghetti is added).
Prep. time: 50 min. *Serves 4.*

Gazpacho

*The extra kick in this gazpacho comes from the wine
vinegar.*

4 large tomatoes,
chopped

1 clove garlic, peeled

1 cucumber, peeled,
chopped

1 green pepper, seeded,
chopped

2 scallions with tops,
sliced

2 T. wine vinegar

1 egg white

1 T. frozen concentrated
apple juice

¼ t. pepper

Per Serving		
Total Fat	1	gm
Saturated	0.1	gm
Unsaturated	0.9	gm
Cholesterol	0	mg
Sodium	29	mg
Carbohydrate	12	gm
Protein	3	gm
Fiber	3	gm
Calories	55	

Place all ingredients in an electric food processor or
blender. Process, but do not purée completely. Chill.
Serve with additional diced cucumber and sliced
scallions on top, if desired.
Prep. time: 35 min. *Serves 4.*

Traditional Potato Soup

Per Serving

Total Fat	0.3 gm
Saturated	0 gm
Unsaturated	0.3 gm
Cholesterol	0 mg
Sodium	19 mg
Carbohydrate	32 gm
Protein	3 gm
Fiber	5 gm
Calories	141

One potato, two potato, three potato, four...

1 large potato

1 ½ c. water

¼ t. basil

¼ clove garlic, minced

¼ small onion, chopped

¼ t. white pepper

½ c. carrot, chopped

½ c. bell pepper, chopped

Pinch of poppy seeds

Cook potato. Blend with remaining ingredients, except poppy seeds, until smooth. Or, if you prefer, leave chunks of cooked potato, carrot, and bell pepper. Add water. Simmer until tender. Garnish with poppy seeds.
Prep. time: 1 hour. *Serves 2.*

Creamy Potato Soup

Per Serving

Total Fat	0.1 gm
Saturated	0 gm
Unsaturated	0.1 gm
Cholesterol	1 mg
Sodium	36 mg
Carbohydrate	17 gm
Protein	4 gm
Fiber	1 gm
Calories	84

This version of the potato soup is slightly creamier than the traditional version, but just as tasty.

1 lb. potatoes

1 medium onion

1 quart water

½ c. skim milk

1 c. nonfat yogurt

⅛ t. pepper

1 T. chopped fresh parsley

½ t. paprika

Peel and slice potatoes and onion. Put into a saucepan with water; cover and bring to a boil. Reduce heat and simmer until vegetables are soft, about 35 min. Pour water and vegetables into an electric blender and blend at high speed. Stir in milk, yogurt, and pepper. Heat on low temperature, but do not boil. Serve with a sprinkling of chopped parsley and paprika.
Prep. time: 1 hour and 15 min. *Serves 8.*

Basic Cream Soup

This soup not only makes a wonderful base for the next few recipes, it's also creamy enough to have all by itself.

6 medium carrots, chopped

2 medium onions, chopped

1 small bell pepper, chopped

3 zucchini, chopped

3 stalks celery, chopped

2 large tomatoes, chopped

1 c. parsley, chopped

2 c. nonfat milk

Per Serving		
Total Fat	1	gm
Saturated	0.2	gm
Unsaturated	1.8	gm
Cholesterol	1	mg
Sodium	114	mg
Carbohydrate	31	gm
Protein	7	gm
Fiber	9	gm
Calories	147	

Simmer all vegetables in 1 c. of nonfat milk until carrots are tender. Drain off liquid and blend vegetables until creamy, adding liquid as needed. Add remaining milk and heat through.
Prep. time: 40 min. *Serves 4.*

Still confused about 2% milk? You might think it means 98% fat free, but it doesn't. The number "2%" refers to the percentage of fat by weight. In 2% milk, there are 121 calories and 5 grams of fat per cup. Since each gram of fat has 9 calories, fat constitutes 45 of the 121 total calories, that is, 37% of the calories are fat. 2% is far from a low-fat food!

Spinach Cream Soup

Per Serving

Total Fat	1	gm
Saturated	0.2	gm
Unsaturated	0.8	gm
Cholesterol	0.5	mg
Sodium	77	mg
Carbohydrate	12	gm
Protein	4	gm
Fiber	2	gm
Calories	60	

Using fresh spinach, rather than frozen, gives this soup a lot more flavor.

2 c. Basic Cream Soup (see previous page)

1 package thawed frozen spinach, or 1 lb. fresh spinach, cleaned, stemmed and chopped

½ T. pepper

½ T. nutmeg

¼ T. allspice

¼ t. marjoram

¼ t. thyme

⅛ c. lemon juice

Mix ingredients well, and bring to a boil slowly. Remove from heat and serve immediately.
Prep. time: 1 hour. *Serves 4.*

Tomato Cream Soup

Per Serving

Total Fat	1	gm
Saturated	0.3	gm
Unsaturated	0.7	gm
Cholesterol	3	mg
Sodium	140	mg
Carbohydrate	31	gm
Protein	10	gm
Fiber	6	gm
Calories	156	

One spoonful of this and you'll be reliving your childhood in no time.

1 c. nonfat milk

1 t. flour

1 c. Basic Cream Soup (see previous page)

1 c. unsalted tomato purée

1/3 c. parsley

1/3 t. onion powder

1/3 t. cloves

1/3 t. pepper

1 T. plain nonfat yogurt

Heat the milk in a saucepan. Slowly mix the flour into hot milk, stirring to keep lumps from forming. Add the remaining ingredients, except yogurt. Mix well. Top with 1 T. yogurt.
Prep. time: 1 hour. *Serves 2.*

Carrot Cream Soup

This is a wonderful first course for special occasions.

2 c. Basic Cream Soup
(see page 213)

¾ c. grated carrot

⅓ c. lemon juice

¼ t. tarragon

¼ t. pepper

2 T. plain low-fat yogurt

Per Serving		
Total Fat	1	gm
Saturated	0.1	gm
Unsaturated	0.9	gm
Cholesterol	1	mg
Sodium	93	mg
Carbohydrate	25	gm
Protein	6	gm
Fiber	6	gm
Calories	117	

Combine all ingredients, except yogurt, and bring to a boil slowly. Remove from heat. Serve with a tablespoon of yogurt on top of each serving. Prep. time: 1 hour. *Serves 2.*

You can't get too much beta-carotene. Studies have shown no significant toxicity, even at very high doses. The only side effect you'd get from eating too many carrots or getting too much beta-carotene would be orange-colored skin, since your epithelial cells would be storing carotene. If it happens to you, it's called, "Carotenodermia," and it's harmless.

Cream of Vegetable Soup

Serve this with muffins or bread and you've got a light supper with very little clean-up.

2 c. frozen mixed
vegetables (peas,
carrots, corn, limas,
green beans)

4 c. water

4 T. whole wheat flour

1 T. vegetable broth
seasoning

2 t. olive oil

Per Serving		
Total Fat	6	gm
Saturated	0.7	gm
Unsaturated	5.3	gm
Cholesterol	0	mg
Sodium	79	mg
Carbohydrate	36	gm
Protein	9	gm
Fiber	9	gm
Calories	220	

Partially thaw frozen vegetables. Blend with water; add remaining ingredients, except oil. Blend until smooth. Cook in saucepan on low heat until bubbly, 12 to 15 min. Stir often. Add oil and serve. Prep. time: 35 min. *Serves 2.*

Cream of Cucumber Soup

Per Serving

Total Fat	1	gm
Saturated	0.1	gm
Unsaturated	0.9	gm
Cholesterol	2	mg
Sodium	60	mg
Carbohydrate	7	gm
Protein	4	gm
Fiber	1	gm
Calories	43	

Serve this creamy soup in the summer, when fresh cucumbers are ripe and plentiful.

2 cucumbers, peeled

1 c. Salt-Free Chicken Broth (see page 202)

½ c. nonfat plain yogurt

½ c. skim milk

½ c. buttermilk

1 scallion, thinly sliced, including tops

1 T. chopped fresh parsley

¼ t. dried dill weed

⅛ t. Tabasco sauce

Cut cucumbers lengthwise and remove seeds. Place all ingredients in a food processor or blender; purée. Chill until ready to serve.

Prep. time: 3 hours. *Serves 6.*

Tomato-Rice Soup

Per Serving

Total Fat	1	gm
Saturated	0.1	gm
Unsaturated	0.9	gm
Cholesterol	0	mg
Sodium	23	mg
Carbohydrate	26	gm
Protein	3	gm
Fiber	3	gm
Calories	119	

8 large fresh tomatoes

3 beef marrow bones, no meat

2 quarts water

2 onions, finely diced

1 clove garlic, finely minced

½ t. paprika

¼ t. pepper

¼ t. dried basil

2 T. lemon juice

1 T. cider vinegar

2 T. frozen apple juice concentrate

3 T. cream of rice cereal

½ c. uncooked rice

Briefly dip tomatoes into boiling water and peel. Cut up and place in a deep pot. Add beef marrow bones, water, onions, garlic, paprika, pepper, basil, lemon juice, vinegar, and apple juice concentrate. Simmer for 2 hours, covered. Stir some of the hot soup into the cream of rice cereal until smooth, then add this mixture to the soup, stirring as it thickens. Add rice and cook for 30 min. more.

Prep. time: 4 hours. *Serves 8.*

Fish Chowder

2 potatoes, peeled and
 cubed

1 onion, thinly sliced

1 sprig dill weed, finely
 chopped

2 c. water

1 lb. fish fillets, such as
 flounder or cod

2 c. skim milk

¼ t. dried thyme

¼ t. white pepper

Per Serving

Total Fat	1	gm
Saturated	0.1	gm
Unsaturated	0.9	gm
Cholesterol	25	mg
Sodium	67	mg
Carbohydrate	14	gm
Protein	14	gm
Fiber	2	gm
Calories	130	

Simmer potatoes, onions, and dill weed in water in a
large covered saucepan until potatoes are soft, about
15 min. Cut fish fillets into small chunks and add to
potatoes. Stir in milk, thyme, and pepper. Simmer,
covered, for an additional 15 to 20 min., stirring
occasionally. Serve at once.
Prep. time: 1 hour. *Serves 8.*

Vegetable Soup

3 whole cloves of garlic,
 chopped

¼ c. chopped fresh basil

¼ c. chopped parsley

½ c. chopped celery

½ c. chopped onion

6 c. Salt-Free Chicken
 Broth (see page 202)

1 c. water

1 can (28 oz.) whole
 tomatoes, no salt

3 small red potatoes,
 cubed small

½ carrot, thinly sliced

1 zucchini, sliced

1 yellow squash, sliced

1 head broccoli, cut up in
 small pieces

1 t. pepper

Per Serving

Total Fat	3	gm
Saturated	0.8	gm
Unsaturated	2.2	gm
Cholesterol	30	mg
Sodium	85	mg
Carbohydrate	29	gm
Protein	15	gm
Fiber	7	gm
Calories	196	

In a large, non-stick stockpot, brown the garlic,
basil, parsley, celery, and onion for about 2 minutes,
stirring to evenly brown. Add chicken broth, water,
and tomatoes. Bring to a gentle boil. Add the
potatoes and carrots; cook until tender. Add
remaining vegetables. Simmer on medium heat for
about 40 min.
Prep. time: 1 hour and 30 min. *Serves 6.*

Sandwiches

Vegetable Sandwich

Per Serving		
Total Fat	19	gm
Saturated	2	gm
Unsaturated	17	gm
Cholesterol	0	mg
Sodium	369	mg
Carbohydrate	34	gm
Protein	11	gm
Fiber	3	gm
Calories	326	

It's got crunch. It's got flavor. It's filling. It's the greatest.

2 slices whole grain
   bread
1 t. Tofu Mayonnaise
   (see page 97)
1 t. chopped mushrooms
2-3 tomato slices
1 large lettuce leaf

1 T. scallions, chopped
3 cucumber slices
1 T. alfalfa sprouts
1 pinch Salt Sub
   (see page 235)

Spread whole grain bread with Tofu Mayonnaise.
Layer with vegetables. Sprinkle with Salt Sub.
Prep. time: 15 min. *Serves 1.*

Lentil-Potato Burgers

Per Serving		
Total Fat	9	gm
Saturated	1.1	gm
Unsaturated	7.9	gm
Cholesterol	0	mg
Sodium	488	mg
Carbohydrate	81	gm
Protein	18	gm
Fiber	11	gm
Calories	451	

Dress this healthy burger up with condiments for that old-fashioned taste.

2 c. mashed potatoes
   (4 medium potatoes)
1 onion, chopped
½ t. sage
2 c. cooked lentils

½ c. chopped pecans
6 whole wheat buns
Mustard, catsup, onion
   slices, tomato slices,
   lettuce, as desired

Preheat oven to 400° F. Peel potatoes, cook until done;
blend with small amount of cooking water in blender
until smooth. Combine onion and sage in a non-stick
pan; simmer to partially cook the onion. Add lentils
and pecans; mix well. Add lentil mixture to potatoes
and form into small burgers; place on a non-stick
cookie sheet. Cover with foil; bake for 20 min. Serve
on whole wheat burger buns with mustard, catsup,
onion slices, tomato slices, and lettuce, as desired.
Prep. time: 1 hour and 30 min. *Makes 6 burgers.*

Egg-White Salad Sandwich

This recipe is great anytime, but it's especially handy around Easter.

12 hard-boiled egg whites, chopped

2 stalks celery, chopped

¼ c. green onions, chopped

¼ c. green pepper, chopped

¼ t. cayenne pepper

1 T. parsley, chopped

¼ t. mustard powder

1 t. vegetable broth seasoning

½ c. White Miracle Blend (see page 230)

12 slices whole grain bread

Per Serving		
Total Fat	6	gm
Saturated	0.4	gm
Unsaturated	5.6	gm
Cholesterol	0.2	mg
Sodium	501	mg
Carbohydrate	30	gm
Protein	16	gm
Fiber	8	gm
Calories	320	

Combine all ingredients, except Miracle Blend. Add Miracle Blend a little at a time, until salad has desired moistness. Spread salad on bread.
Prep. time: 15 min. *Makes 6 sandwiches.*

Sprout Sandwich

This is a great sandwich for a picnic, when the vegetables are at their peak of freshness. You'll be amazed that a non-meat sandwich can taste so good.

4 slices whole grain bread

2 t. prepared mustard

¼ avocado, sliced

1 t. vegetable broth seasoning

1 small tomato, sliced thin

2 c. alfalfa sprouts

Lettuce leaves, unsweetened pineapple rings, orange or apple slices, optional

Per Serving		
Total Fat	7	gm
Saturated	0.1	gm
Unsaturated	0.9	gm
Cholesterol	0	mg
Sodium	430	mg
Carbohydrate	30	gm
Protein	8	gm
Fiber	11	gm
Calories	200	

Spread 2 bread slices with ½ t. mustard. On remaining 2 slices of bread, layer: ⅛ avocado, ½ t. vegetable broth seasoning, ½ tomato, and a handful of sprouts. Top with the other slice of bread and cut in half. Serve each sandwich on a plate with lettuce leaf and unsweetened pineapple ring or orange or apple slices, if desired.
Prep. time: 15 min. *Serves 2.*

Falafel Burgers

½ c. bulgur

1 c. boiling water

2 c. canned garbanzo beans, drained

3 cloves garlic, minced

¼ c. lemon juice

1 t. vegetable broth seasoning

¼ t. Tabasco

3 egg whites

1 t. sesame oil

½ c. dry bread crumbs

6 pita bread pockets

12 fresh tomato slices

6 T. Tahini Sauce (see recipe below

Soak bulgur in boiling water for 20 min; drain. In blender or food processor, combine garbanzo beans, garlic, lemon juice, vegetable broth seasoning, and Tabasco. In a large bowl, beat egg whites and oil. Mix in bread crumbs, puréed garbanzo mixture and drained bulgur. Shape mixture into 6 patties. On a non-stick griddle, cook patties about 5 min. on each side. Serve immediately in pita pockets with tomato slices and 1 T. Tahini Sauce for each pita.
Prep. time: 45 min. *Serves 3 (2 burgers each).*

Tahini Sauce
Sesame tahini is a nut butter made from grinding sesame seeds into a paste the very same way peanut butter is made. Use raw tahini and always keep it refrigerated.

2 T. water

2 t. lemon juice or vinegar

½ t. flax oil

3 T. raw sesame tahini

1-2 cloves garlic, minced

Dash of cayenne pepper

In a small bowl, stir water, lemon juice, and oil with tahi until thoroughly mixed. Stir in garlic and cayenne peppe
Prep. time: 5 min. *Makes 6 tablespoons.*

Bean Burgers

This is one of the very best, most nutritious "burgers" we've ever come across. You'll be happily surprised at how delicious this outstanding recipe is.

¾ c. cooked garbanzo beans

⅓ c. cooked kidney beans

½ c. cooked brown rice

1 onion, chopped

1 carrot, grated

1 stalk celery, chopped

1 T. Salt Sub (see page 235)

3 T. brewer's yeast

4 egg whites, beaten

Tomato sauce, optional

Per Serving		
Total Fat	1	gm
Saturated	0.1	gm
Unsaturated	0.9	gm
Cholesterol	0	mg
Sodium	193	mg
Carbohydrate	24	gm
Protein	10	gm
Fiber	6	gm
Calories	143	

Combine garbanzo and kidney beans, rice, onion, carrot, and celery in food processor or blender for an instant (leave chunky, but well blended). Add Salt Sub, yeast, and egg whites with a fork to blend well. Form into 4 patties. Brown on a non-stick griddle— in some tomato sauce, if desired. Serve hot or cold. Prep. time: 50 min. *Serves 2 (2 burgers each).*

Grilled Pineapple-Banana Sandwich

2 T. crushed unsweetened pineapple

4 slices whole grain bread

1 ripe banana, sliced lengthwise

½ t. cinnamon

Per Serving		
Total Fat	3	gm
Saturated	0.1	gm
Unsaturated	2.9	gm
Cholesterol	0	mg
Sodium	357	mg
Carbohydrate	41	gm
Protein	6	gm
Fiber	7	gm
Calories	196	

Spread pineapple on 2 slices of bread. Cover with strips of banana, then sprinkle each slice with ¼ t. cinnamon. Top with remaining 2 slices of bread. Grill on a preheated non-stick griddle until browned. Prep. time: 10 min. *Serves 2.*

223

Lentil-Spread Sandwich

Per Serving

Total Fat	2	gm
Saturated	0	gm
Unsaturated	2	gm
Cholesterol	0	mg
Sodium	60	mg
Carbohydrate	15	gm
Protein	7	gm
Fiber	4	gm
Calories	100	

1 c. cooked lentils

1 carrot, cooked

1 small tomato

1 T. cider

2 T. vegetable broth
   seasoning

1 t. Salt Sub
   (see page 235)

1 T. naturally prepared
   mustard

1 T. tomato juice

Lettuce leaves and
   tomato slices, optional

Blend all ingredients but the lettuce and tomato until smooth. Add tomato juice as needed to keep from being too dry. Use liberally as sandwich filling along with lettuce and tomatoes, as desired. Prep. time: 10 min. *Serves 4.*

Sloppy Moes

Per Serving

Total Fat	5	gm
Saturated	0.7	gm
Unsaturated	4.3	gm
Cholesterol	0	mg
Sodium	22	mg
Carbohydrate	41	gm
Protein	3	gm
Fiber	4	gm
Calories	219	

1 c. cooked barley

¾ c. unsalted spaghetti
   sauce

1 apple, peeled and cut
   into bite-size chunks

1 T. vegetable broth
   seasoning

2 slices whole grain
   bread, toasted

Lettuce leaves and
   orange, pineapple or
   tomato slices, optional

Mix the cooked barley with the spaghetti sauce and raw apple. Mix in the vegetable broth seasoning. Serve on toast. Garnish with a lettuce leaf and orange, pineapple, or tomato slices. Prep. time: 20 min. *Serves 2.*

Hummus Sandwich

This Middle Eastern treat is so well liked they should call it a "Yummus Sandwich."

¾ c. mashed garbanzo
  beans

1 T. sesame tahini

2 cloves garlic, minced

1 T. chopped fresh
  parsley

1 t. vinegar

4 slices whole grain
  bread

4 slices tomato

Per Serving		
Total Fat	7	gm
Saturated	0.6	gm
Unsaturated	6.4	gm
Cholesterol	0	mg
Sodium	476	mg
Carbohydrate	34	gm
Protein	8	gm
Fiber	9	gm
Calories	219	

In a blender, food processor, meat grinder, or with a potato masher, mix all ingredients together, except the bread and tomato. Spread mixture evenly on two slices of bread, layer with tomato slices, and top with remaining slices of bread.
Prep. time: 10 min. *Serves 2.*

Grilled Banana and Honey Sandwich

Also known as "The KingWich." We love this sandwich all the more because it's a low-fat spin-off of Elvis Presley's favorite lunch.

1 ripe banana

2 slices whole grain
  bread

1 T. honey

¼ t. cinnamon, optional

Per Serving		
Total Fat	3	gm
Saturated	0.2	gm
Unsaturated	2.8	gm
Cholesterol	0	mg
Sodium	358	mg
Carbohydrate	70	gm
Protein	7	gm
Fiber	8	gm
Calories	306	

Mash the banana with a fork. Spread thickly on the bread. Drizzle with honey. Sprinkle with cinnamon, if desired. Grill under broiler until bubbly.
Prep. time: 15 min. *Serves 1.*

Veggie Salad Spread

This makes a great spread for a cocktail party.

Per Serving		
Total Fat	18	gm
Saturated	1.7	gm
Unsaturated	16.3	gm
Cholesterol	0	mg
Sodium	21	mg
Carbohydrate	14	gm
Protein	7	gm
Fiber	5	gm
Calories	226	

2 carrots, grated

3 zucchini, grated

2 T. Traditional French Dressing (see page 101)

½ c. parsley, finely chopped

½ c. pecans, finely chopped

½ c. sunflower seeds, finely chopped

Moisten carrots and zucchini with Traditional French Dressing. Mix with remaining ingredients. Serve on whole grain bread or crackers, in pita bread, or on a bed of crisp greens, as desired.
Prep. time: 25 min. *Serves 4.*

Skim Milk Ricotta Sandwich

Per Serving		
Total Fat	5	gm
Saturated	1.5	gm
Unsaturated	3.5	gm
Cholesterol	10	mg
Sodium	395	mg
Carbohydrate	43	gm
Protein	9	gm
Fiber	8	gm
Calories	241	

2 T. skim milk ricotta cheese, crumbled

2 slices whole grain bread

⅛ c. chopped dates

Spread a thick layer of ricotta on the bread. Sprinkle with the dates. Can be eaten cold or broiled.
Prep. time: 5 min. *Serves 1.*

Sandwiches were named for the Earl of Sandwich, an English nobleman who lived in the early 1700s. One day while he was playing cards, he ordered a bit of roast meat between two slices of bread—and thus the sandwich was born.

Sauces & Extras

Miracle Blend—White

This and the following Brown Blend are tangy options to mayonnaise.

½ c. nonfat milk

3 T. whey powder

8 T. hulled, raw sesame seeds

1 T. natural mustard

1 T. cider vinegar

Blend ingredients until creamy smooth. Use instead of mayonnaise. Keeps about a week in the refrigerator.
Prep. time: 5 min. Serving size is 2 T. *Makes 1 cup.*

Miracle Blend—Brown

Miracle Blend Brown can spruce up any sandwich.

½ c. apple or pear juice

1 ½ T. cider vinegar

1 heaping T. vegetable broth seasoning

2 heaping T. unhulled raw sesame seeds

Blend ingredients until creamy smooth. Use instead of mayonnaise. Keeps in refrigerator about a week.
Prep. time: 5 min. Serving size is 2 T. *Makes 1 cup.*

White Sauce

Either white sauce is wonderful over vegetables.

2 c. Salt-Free Chicken
  Broth (see page 202)

2 c. dry nonfat milk

1 T. dry white wine

2 ½ T. cornstarch

1 t. rosemary

⅛ t. curry powder

1 c. water

Per Serving		
Total Fat	1	gm
Saturated	0.1	gm
Unsaturated	0.9	gm
Cholesterol	2	mg
Sodium	232	mg
Carbohydrate	11	gm
Protein	7	gm
Fiber	0.1	gm
Calories	77	

Heat chicken broth to a boil in a saucepan. While this is warming, combine remaining ingredients in a bowl and mix until smooth; add slowly to the simmering broth, stirring occasionally until sauce is thick and smooth.
Prep. time: 20 min. *Makes 3 cups. Serves 4.*

Sauterne White Sauce

Sauterne is a rich, sweet, white table wine of France. The alcohol evaporates when it's cooked, and what's left is a harmless carbohydrate that flavors the sauce like nothing else can.

1 ⅓ c. liquid nonfat milk

⅓ c. dry nonfat milk

1 t. soy or tamari sauce

1 T. onion powder

1 T. arrowroot

1 t. garlic powder

2 ½ T. sauterne wine

Dash of dill weed

Per Serving		
Total Fat	0.2	gm
Saturated	0.1	gm
Unsaturated	0.1	gm
Cholesterol	2	mg
Sodium	158	mg
Carbohydrate	11	gm
Protein	5	gm
Fiber	0.1	gm
Calories	73	

Heat liquid nonfat milk in a saucepan, stirring occasionally. Combine all other ingredients to make a smooth paste. When milk in saucepan simmers, add paste, stirring constantly until thickened.
Prep. time: 25 min. *Makes 1 ½ cups. Serves 4.*

Mushroom Gravy

Per Serving

Total Fat	1	gm
Saturated	0.3	gm
Unsaturated	0.7	gm
Cholesterol	0.1	mg
Sodium	302	mg
Carbohydrate	9	gm
Protein	2	gm
Fiber	3	gm
Calories	54	

A sassy mushroom gravy with no lumps!

¾ c. chopped onions
1 T. vegetable broth
  seasoning
1 T. arrowroot
1 c. water
1 c. cooked mushroom
  pieces

1 T. white wine
¼ t. black pepper
1 T. salsa
1 t. crude, expeller-
  pressed sesame oil

In a non-stick saucepan coated with nonfat cooking spray, sauté onions. Dissolve vegetable broth seasoning and arrowroot into 1 c. water and add to onions. Add mushrooms. Cook gently until thickened (it will only take a minute or so). Add white wine, pepper, salsa, and oil. Serve over Vegeloaf, burgers, or similar dishes.
Prep. time: 15 min. *Makes 2 cups. Serves 4.*

Lemon Sauce

Per Serving

Total Fat	14	gm
Saturated	1.9	gm
Unsaturated	12.1	gm
Cholesterol	0	mg
Sodium	4	mg
Carbohydrate	9	gm
Protein	0.1	gm
Fiber	0.4	gm
Calories	152	

This great sauce doubles for hollandaise. No one knows the difference and everyone wants the recipe.

2 T. arrowroot
½ t. Salt Sub
  (see page 235)
1 c. water

2 T. olive oil
2 T. lemon juice
1 t. grated lemon rind

Stir arrowroot, Salt Sub, and water together in sauce pan over medium heat. Stir constantly until thick. Simmer, covered on low heat, for 10 min. Remove from heat and blend in oil, lemon juice, and lemon rind. Beat well with wire whisk. Serve hot on vegetables.
Prep. time: 25 min. *Makes 1 ½ cups. Serves 6.*

Marinara Sauce

An outstanding pasta topping. Make a big batch and refrigerate it for the week.

3 cloves garlic, peeled, minced

8 ripe tomatoes, peeled, chopped, or 2 cans (28 oz.) whole tomatoes

¾ t. crushed oregano

½ t. chopped fresh parsley

½ t. chopped fresh basil

Per Serving		
Total Fat	3	gm
Saturated	0.4	gm
Unsaturated	2.6	gm
Cholesterol	0	mg
Sodium	73	mg
Carbohydrate	39	gm
Protein	7	gm
Fiber	10	gm
Calories	176	

In a non-stick skillet coated with nonfat cooking spray, sauté garlic until tender. Stir in tomatoes, and bring to a boil over medium heat. Add herbs; simmer for 15 min. Serve over pasta of your choice. Prep. time: 30 min. *Makes 3 cups. Serves 2.*

Italian Tomato Sauce

The mushrooms and peppers bulk up this sauce so it's every bit as good as a meaty sauce—and better for you.

1 brown onion

3 cloves garlic, diced

1 bell pepper, diced

1 c. mushrooms

3 T. water

1 large can (28 oz.) tomato purée

1 can (6 oz.) no-salt tomato paste

½ t. Italian seasoning, or ⅛ t. each: oregano, basil, thyme, and marjoram (add more or less to taste)

Per Serving		
Total Fat	1	gm
Saturated	0.1	gm
Unsaturated	0.9	gm
Cholesterol	0	mg
Sodium	72	mg
Carbohydrate	36	gm
Protein	7	gm
Fiber	8	gm
Calories	156	

In a large covered pot, sauté onion, garlic, bell pepper, and mushrooms in water until tender. Add remaining ingredients. Simmer for 1 hour. Prep. time: 1 hour and 20 min. Makes 4 cups. *Serves 4.*

Italian Spaghetti Sauce

Per Serving

Total Fat	1	gm
Saturated	0.1	gm
Unsaturated	0.9	gm
Cholesterol	0	mg
Sodium	80	mg
Carbohydrate	28	gm
Protein	5	gm
Fiber	6	gm
Calories	125	

You'll find this is the best spaghetti sauce yet—and you won't even miss the meat.

1 small can tomato paste (6 oz.)

4 cans water (24 oz., total)

4 large ripe tomatoes, peeled and blended coarsely

3 stalks celery, chopped, tops included

1 green pepper, chopped

1 onion, chopped

½ c. carrot, very finely chopped

1 T. basil

1 t. oregano

2 T. garlic powder (or 4 cloves fresh garlic, minced)

1 c. coarsely chopped mushrooms

Simmer ingredients for 30 min. to an hour. Serve over any pasta.
Prep. time: 55 min. Makes 4 cups. *Serves 4.*

Salsa

Per Serving

Total Fat	0.4	gm
Saturated	0	gm
Unsaturated	0.4	gm
Cholesterol	0	mg
Sodium	30	mg
Carbohydrate	10	gm
Protein	2	gm
Fiber	3	gm
Calories	48	

With just a few minutes of prep time, you'll have guests eating out of your hand with this salsa.

1 small can chopped sweet red bell peppers

1 large onion, chopped

1 small can chopped green chili peppers

1 small can peeled tomatoes, chopped

Salt Sub (see page 235)

Tabasco sauce

Combine first 4 ingredients. Add Salt Sub and Tabasco to taste. Serve with baked tortilla chips.
Prep. time: 10 min. *Makes 4 cups. Serves 8.*

Salt Sub

This is a spicy, sassy seasoning that will make you throw your old salt shaker away! Make a big batch of it; you'll find yourself using it all the time.

4 parts onion powder

2 parts paprika

2 parts garlic powder

3 parts cayenne pepper

Mix together. Use in place of salt.
Prep. time: 5 min.

Desserts

Fresh Fruit Delight

Per Serving

Total Fat	0.3	gm
Saturated	0.1	gm
Unsaturated	0.2	gm
Cholesterol	1	mg
Sodium	48	mg
Carbohydrate	18	gm
Protein	4	gm
Fiber	2	gm
Calories	82	

Prepare in pretty parfait glasses and your guests will be delighted. If you don't like dairy products, replace the yogurt with soygurt, available at most health food stores. It's delicious.

1 banana, sliced

½ cantaloupe, cut into 1-inch chunks

1 kiwi fruit, peeled and sliced thin

1 c. plain nonfat yogurt

¼ t. ground nutmeg

1 t. grated orange rind

½ t. vanilla extract

Combine all fruit and spoon into 6 stemmed sherbet glasses. Separately, combine yogurt, nutmeg, orange rind, and vanilla; spoon over fruit. Top with a dash of nutmeg.
Prep. time: 15 min. *Serves 6.*

Baked Apple with Lemon-Raisin Topping

Per Serving

Total Fat	1	gm
Saturated	0.2	gm
Unsaturated	0.8	gm
Cholesterol	1	mg
Sodium	11	mg
Carbohydrate	28	gm
Protein	1	gm
Fiber	3	gm
Calories	110	

What a sneaky way of giving children something that looks and tastes like dessert, but has so much nutritional value.

4 medium baking apples

4 t. frozen apple juice concentrate

¼ t. cinnamon

⅛ t. nutmeg

4 T. low-fat lemon yogurt

2 t. seedless white raisins

Preheat oven to 350° F. Core apples from stem side almost through the other side. Remove pits. Remove ½-inch of apple peel from top. Fill each apple cavity with 1 t. frozen apple juice concentrate. Sprinkle with cinnamon and nutmeg. Place in a small baking dish. Pour ½-inch water around apples. Bake for 20 min., or until apples are soft but still holding their shape. Serve warm or cold with a topping of lemon yogurt and a sprinkling of raisins.
Prep. time: 40 min. *Serves 4.*

Carob-Mint Mousse

An elegant dessert that chocolate lovers (and all kids) love.

2 envelopes unflavored gelatin

2 T. unsweetened carob powder

1 c. thawed frozen apple juice concentrate

2 ½ t. vanilla extract

3 ¼ c. liquid nonfat milk

⅓ c. dry nonfat milk

¼ t. mint flakes

Fruit slices or sprig of fresh mint, optional

Per Serving		
Total Fat	1	gm
Saturated	0.2	gm
Unsaturated	0.8	gm
Cholesterol	3	mg
Sodium	126	mg
Carbohydrate	38	gm
Protein	10	gm
Fiber	0.4	gm
Calories	193	

Place gelatin and carob powder in a large bowl; add ¼ c. of the apple juice, and mix well. Heat remaining apple juice and vanilla extract to a boil in a saucepan; turn down the heat. Add gelatin and carob mixture; stir constantly over low heat for about 5 min. Refrigerate until cool. Place milk (both liquid and dry), mint flakes, and gelatin mixture in a blender, half at a time if necessary, and blend. When fluffy and light, transfer to a mixing bowl; chill in freezer until cold and thickened—not frozen. Whip with an electric mixer. Return to freezer to chill, but do not freeze. Whip once more before serving. Garnish with fruit slices or a sprig of fresh mint, if desired.
Prep. time: 50 min. *Serves 5.*

Ambrosia Delight

Light, fresh, and simple. This is a favorite.

½ c. plain nonfat yogurt

Juice of 1 orange

2 T. honey

2 c. sliced ripe bananas

2 c. fresh pineapple chunks

1 papaya, peeled, seeded, and cubed

Per Serving		
Total Fat	1	gm
Saturated	0.2	gm
Unsaturated	0.8	gm
Cholesterol	0.4	mg
Sodium	20	mg
Carbohydrate	43	gm
Protein	3	gm
Fiber	3	gm
Calories	174	

Combine yogurt, orange juice, and honey. Pour over mixed fruits.
Prep. time: 15 min. *Serves 2.*

Rice Pudding

Per Serving

Total Fat	1	gm
Saturated	0.2	gm
Unsaturated	0.8	gm
Cholesterol	1	mg
Sodium	43	mg
Carbohydrate	27	gm
Protein	4	gm
Fiber	1	gm
Calories	124	

Children love this!

1 ½ c. nonfat milk

4 egg whites

2 T. honey

½ t. nutmeg

1 t. cinnamon

1 T. tapioca granules

2 c. cooked brown rice

1 c. raisins

Preheat oven to 350° F. In a double boiler, heat milk. In a bowl, beat egg whites lightly. Add honey, nutmeg, cinnamon, and tapioca to egg whites. Slowly add hot milk to egg white mixture, stirring constantly, about 10 min., or until mixture starts to thicken. Remove from heat and add rice. Mix well. Fold in raisins. Pour into a pan-sprayed, non-stick, 2-quart baking dish. Bake for 15 min., or until set. Serve warm or cold.
Prep. time: 50 min. *Makes 10 ½-cup servings.*

Banana Pudding

Per Serving

Total Fat	0.2	gm
Saturated	0.1	gm
Unsaturated	0.1	gm
Cholesterol	1	mg
Sodium	39	mg
Carbohydrate	20	gm
Protein	2	gm
Fiber	0.4	gm
Calories	89	

Look for bananas with brownish skins because the more ripened a banana is, the better it is for this recipe.

1 quart nonfat milk

½ c. honey

6 T. arrowroot

1 t. vanilla

1 ½ c. mashed ripe banana

½ c. boiling water

2 T. agar

Blend milk, honey, arrowroot, and vanilla. Heat until thick. Add milk mixture to mashed banana. In another pan, heat water and agar. Add to milk mixture. Chill and serve. This pudding can be used as a pie filling.
Prep. time: 20 min. *Makes 15 ½-cup servings.*

Agar is a gelatin-like product made from certain seaweeds and is used in cooking for solidifying and thickening. It's the perfect gelatin substitute for vegetarians and it's usually only available in health food stores.

Orange Sherbet

A sweet, tangy touch of citrus that's cool on a hot day.

½ c. nonfat dry milk

1 T. fresh lemon juice

1 t. almond flavoring

1 ¼ c. water

1 can (6 oz.) frozen
    orange juice
    concentrate

¼ c. frozen apple juice
    concentrate

2 egg whites

Per Serving		
Total Fat	0.1	gm
Saturated	0.1	gm
Unsaturated	0	gm
Cholesterol	1	mg
Sodium	41	mg
Carbohydrate	14	gm
Protein	3	gm
Fiber	0.2	gm
Calories	68	

Place dry milk, lemon juice, almond flavoring, and ½ c. water in a mixing bowl; beat until mixture is thick and fluffy. Add frozen orange juice concentrate; beat again. Add ¾ c. water and frozen apple juice concentrate; beat again. Pour mixture into two ice cube trays with separators removed. When mixture is partially frozen, remove and beat again. Beat egg whites until stiff peaks form; fold through orange mixture. Return to freezer until sherbet is frozen firmly.
Prep. time: 1 hour. *Serves 8.*

Orange-Yogurt Mold

1 T. unflavored gelatin

½ c. water

3 c. plain nonfat yogurt

1 large banana

¼ c. frozen orange juice
    concentrate

Per Serving		
Total Fat	0.2	gm
Saturated	0.1	gm
Unsaturated	0.1	gm
Cholesterol	4	mg
Sodium	123	mg
Carbohydrate	27	gm
Protein	12	gm
Fiber	1	gm
Calories	152	

Mix gelatin in ½ c. cold water, and heat to dissolve. In blender, combine gelatin mixture, yogurt, banana, and orange juice concentrate. Pour into mold and refrigerate until set.
Prep. time: 15 min., plus setting time. *Serves 4.*

Bran Muffins

1 ½ c. oat bran
¾ c. whole wheat flour
½ t. cinnamon
1 T. baking powder
4 egg whites

1 T. olive oil
½ c. apple juice concentrate
¾ c. skim milk

Preheat oven to 350° F. Combine dry ingredients with egg whites, oil, apple juice concentrate, and skim milk. Pour into non-stick muffin pans. Bake for 15-20 min.
Prep. time: 40 min. A serving is 1 muffin. *Makes 12 muffins.*

Applesauce Muffins

We serve these at the Institute at nearly every meal because of all the valuable fiber they've got.

1 egg white
1 t. vanilla
2 T. honey
1 t. cinnamon
2 t. baking soda
1 ½ c. unsweetened applesauce

2 t. olive oil
¾ c. oat bran
¾ c. raisins
½ c. water
1 c. whole wheat flour

Preheat oven to 350° F. Combine ingredients with a hand mixer in the order given. Pour into non-stick muffin pans. Bake for 40 min.
Prep. time: 1 hour. A serving is 1 muffin. *Makes 12 muffins.*

Fruit Crisp

Of all the recipes we use at the Institute, this would have to be the most popular.

2 c. fruit (blueberries, apples, peaches, etc.)

¼ c. apple juice concentrate

¼ c. whole wheat flour

½ c. oatmeal, uncooked

2 T. cinnamon

2 T. olive oil

2 T. Butter Buds

¼ c. chopped walnuts

2 T. honey

Per Serving		
Total Fat	11	gm
Saturated	1.3	gm
Unsaturated	9.7	gm
Cholesterol	0	mg
Sodium	100	mg
Carbohydrate	43	gm
Protein	5	gm
Fiber	4	gm
Calories	268	

Preheat oven to 350° F. Place fruit in a non-stick 8 x 8-inch pan; pour apple juice concentrate over fruit. Combine remaining ingredients, except honey; spread over top of fruit. Sprinkle with honey. Bake for 30 min.
Prep. time: 50 min. *Serves 4.*

Peach Cobbler

This is a perfect way to top off a midsummer Sunday evening supper.

1 c. pineapple juice

¾ c. pitted dates

1 t. vanilla

1 t. cinnamon

1 T. tapioca powder

1 bag (20 oz.) Freestone peaches, unsweetened, or equivalent fresh peaches

1 T. whole almonds

¼ c. pitted dates

⅓ c. oatmeal

Per Serving		
Total Fat	1	gm
Saturated	0.1	gm
Unsaturated	0.9	gm
Cholesterol	0	mg
Sodium	1	mg
Carbohydrate	33	gm
Protein	2	gm
Fiber	4	gm
Calories	138	

Preheat oven to 350° F. Blend juice, dates, vanilla, cinnamon, and tapioca. In a non-stick baking dish, layer the peaches; pour juice mixture over all. Grind remaining ingredients as a topping and sprinkle evenly over the top. Bake for 45 min.
Prep. time: 1 hour and 10 min. *Serves 8.*

Oatmeal Cookies

Per Serving

Total Fat	1	gm
Saturated	0.2	gm
Unsaturated	0.8	gm
Cholesterol	0	mg
Sodium	34	mg
Carbohydrate	22	gm
Protein	2	gm
Fiber	1	gm
Calories	106	

Finally! Cookies you can eat.

1 T. olive oil	¾ c. flour
½ c. honey	½ t. baking soda
2 egg whites	1 ½ c. oats
1 T. water	½ c. raisins
1 t. vanilla extract	

Preheat oven to 350° F. Beat oil, honey, egg whites, water, and vanilla extract thoroughly. Add dry ingredients, mix well, and add raisins. Drop by teaspoon onto a non-stick cookie sheet. Bake for 10-15 min. Prep. time: 35 min. A serving is 1 cookie. *Makes 16 cookies.*

Carrot-Raisin-Date Cookies

Per Serving

Total Fat	0.1	gm
Saturated	0	gm
Unsaturated	0.1	gm
Cholesterol	0	mg
Sodium	9	mg
Carbohydrate	8	gm
Protein	1	gm
Fiber	1	gm
Calories	36	

½ c. cooked, mashed carrots	1 t. baking powder
1 t. grated orange rind	½ t. ginger
1 t. lemon juice	¼ t. nutmeg
2 egg whites, stiffly beaten	⅓ c. raisins
1 c. unbleached flour	⅓ c. chopped dates

Preheat oven to 350° F. Combine mashed carrots, orange rind, and lemon juice. Fold through stiffly beaten egg whites. Separately, combine flour, baking powder, ginger, and nutmeg; fold through batter. Carefully add raisins and dates. Drop by teaspoon onto a non-stick cookie sheet. Bake for 12 min., or until lightly brown around the edges.
Prep. time: 35 min. A serving is 1 cookie. *Makes 24 cookies.*

Carob-Date Brownies

Kids adore this chewy, chocolate-like treat.

2 egg whites	3 level T. carob powder
1 T. molasses	½ c. oat bran
1 T. honey	½ c. apple juice
1 ½ t. vanilla	1 c. flour
1 c. zucchini, grated	¾ c. chopped dates

Per Serving

Total Fat	1	gm
Saturated	0.1	gm
Unsaturated	0.9	gm
Cholesterol	0	mg
Sodium	20	mg
Carbohydrate	34	gm
Protein	4	gm
Fiber	4	gm
Calories	139	

Preheat oven to 350° F. Beat together egg whites, molasses, honey, and vanilla for 1 min. Slowly, while beating, add remaining ingredients. Bake in a non-stick 8 x 8-inch brownie pan for 25 min.
Prep. time: 50 min. *Serves 9.*

Applesauce Cake

Slices of red and green apples go beautifully with this dessert.

2 T. liquid Butter Buds	2 egg whites
¼ c. honey	¾ t. cinnamon
¼ c. molasses	1 T. baking powder
1 ¼ c. unsweetened applesauce	½ c. raisins
2 T. olive oil	1 ½ c. whole wheat pastry flour

Per Serving

Total Fat	4	gm
Saturated	0.6	gm
Unsaturated	3.4	gm
Cholesterol	0	mg
Sodium	52	mg
Carbohydrate	43	gm
Protein	4	gm
Fiber	4	gm
Calories	212	

Preheat oven to 350° F. Combine Butter Buds, honey, molasses, applesauce, oil, and egg whites; mix well. Add remaining ingredients. Pour into a non-stick 8-inch loaf pan. Bake for 45-50 min.
Prep. time: 1 hour and 20 min. *Serves 8.*

Berry Cobbler

Per Serving

Total Fat	4	gm
Saturated	0.6	gm
Unsaturated	3.4	gm
Cholesterol	0	mg
Sodium	5	mg
Carbohydrate	36	gm
Protein	3	gm
Fiber	3	gm
Calories	183	

You can use pears instead of apples for a sweet, more mellow flavor.

3 T. tapioca granules

1 ½ c. berry juice, unsweetened (boysenberry, blackberry, or grape)

1 t. vanilla

2 apples or pears, peeled and sliced

1 c. berries (any type)

¼ c. raisins

¾ c. oatmeal

¼ c. raw unhulled sesame seeds

1 t. cinnamon

Preheat oven to 350° F. Mix tapioca with berry juice and vanilla; pour into a glass pie pan coated with nonfat cooking spray. Layer the apple or pear slices on top of the tapioca mixture. Next, layer the berries. Sprinkle with raisins. Mix together oatmeal, sesame seeds, and cinnamon. Sprinkle over top of cobbler. Bake for 30 min. Serve warm.
Prep. time: 55 min. *Serves 6.*

Corn Bread

Per Serving

Total Fat	20	gm
Saturated	2.6	gm
Unsaturated	18.4	gm
Cholesterol	1	mg
Sodium	75	mg
Carbohydrate	70	gm
Protein	11	gm
Fiber	6	gm
Calories	483	

Great with any of the soups in this cookbook, and the perfect thing to dip!

1 c. yellow cornmeal

1 c. whole wheat flour

¼ c. honey

1 T. baking powder

⅓ c. olive oil

2 egg whites

1 c. skim milk

Preheat oven to 400° F. Combine dry ingredients in a bowl; mix well. Stir in remaining ingredients until blended. Pour in a non-stick 8 x 8-inch pan. Bake for 25 min., or until done.
Prep. time: 55 min. *Serves 4.*

Honey-Oatmeal Bars

2 c. uncooked oatmeal
¾ c. unbleached flour
¾ c. whole wheat flour
½ c. honey
1 ripe banana, mashed

½ c. chopped nuts
1 t. cinnamon
¼ t. nutmeg
¼ t. salt

Per Serving		
Total Fat	2	gm
Saturated	0.3	gm
Unsaturated	1.7	gm
Cholesterol	0	mg
Sodium	23	mg
Carbohydrate	17	gm
Protein	2	gm
Fiber	1	gm
Calories	95	

Preheat oven to 375° F. Combine all ingredients in a large bowl. Beat at low speed of electric mixer until mixture is crumbly. Spread over bottom of a non-stick 9 x 13-inch pan. Bake for 25 min. Cool and cut into 2-inch squares.
Prep. time: 55 min. A serving is 1 bar. *Makes 24 bars.*

Banana Bread

4 very ripe bananas, mashed
1 T. honey
1 T. baking powder
2 t. cinnamon

2 c. whole wheat flour
4 egg whites
½ c. chopped walnuts, optional

Per Serving		
Total Fat	1	gm
Saturated	0.2	gm
Unsaturated	0.8	gm
Cholesterol	0	mg
Sodium	36	mg
Carbohydrate	39	gm
Protein	7	gm
Fiber	5	gm
Calories	175	

Preheat oven to 350° F. Mix bananas with honey until creamy. Add baking powder and cinnamon. Gradually add flour. Beat egg whites until fluffy; fold into flour mixture. If desired, add walnuts. Bake in a non-stick loaf pan for 1 hour, or until a toothpick inserted into center comes out clean.
Prep. time: 1 hour and 20 min. *Serves 8.*

Apple-Raisin-Noodle Pudding

Per Serving

Total Fat	2	gm
Saturated	0.6	gm
Unsaturated	1.4	gm
Cholesterol	38	mg
Sodium	191	mg
Carbohydrate	43	gm
Protein	11	gm
Fiber	1	gm
Calories	234	

8 ounces wide noodles, cooked and drained

2 apples, peeled, cored, thinly sliced

2 T. lemon juice

½ t. ground cinnamon

1 c. 1% low-fat cottage cheese

2 T. frozen apple juice concentrate

¼ c. seedless white raisins

1 egg white

Preheat oven to 350° F. Combine cooked noodles with apples, lemon juice, and cinnamon. Separately, combine cottage cheese, apple juice concentrate, and raisins. Beat egg white until soft peaks form; fold through cottage cheese mixture. Fold cheese though noodle mixture. Spoon into a non-stick 8 x 12-inch baking pan. Bake for 35 minutes, or until top is lightly browned.
Prep. time: 1 hour and 10 min. *Serves 6.*

Nutritional Bars

Per Serving

Total Fat	3	gm
Saturated	0.3	gm
Unsaturated	2.7	gm
Cholesterol	0	mg
Sodium	100	mg
Carbohydrate	32	gm
Protein	5	gm
Fiber	3	gm
Calories	159	

2 egg whites

½ c. liquid Butter Buds

⅔ c. thawed frozen apple juice concentrate

½ t. baking soda

1 t. cinnamon

½ t. coriander

⅛ t. cloves

½ c. bran

½ c. whole wheat flour

1 ½ c. rolled oats

½ c. raisins

¼ c. almonds, slivered

1 ½ c. apples, chopped

Preheat oven to 350° F. Cream together egg whites, Butter Buds, and apple juice concentrate. Add the baking soda, cinnamon, coriander, and cloves. Beat well. Gradually add bran, flour, and oats. Mix well. Add raisins, almonds, and apples. Press dough into a non-stick cookie sheet. Bake for 20 min. or until done. Cut into bars.
Prep. time: 35 min. *Serves 12.*

Carrot-Zucchini Bread

4 egg whites, beaten
¾ c. honey
1 ½ t. liquid lecithin
½ t. baking soda
½ t. baking powder

¼ t. ground ginger
1 c. carrots, grated
1 c. zucchini, shredded
1 ½ c. whole wheat flour

Per Serving		
Total Fat	1	gm
Saturated	0.1	gm
Unsaturated	0.9	gm
Cholesterol	0	mg
Sodium	88	mg
Carbohydrate	44	gm
Protein	5	gm
Fiber	4	gm
Calories	192	

Preheat oven to 350° F. Mix egg whites with honey and lecithin. Add baking soda and powder. Add ginger. Stir in carrots and zucchini. Gradually add the flour. Bake in a non-stick loaf pan for 1 hour. Prep. time: 1 hour and 20 min. *Serves 8.*

Carrot Cookies

½ c. olive oil
½ c. honey
2 egg whites
1 c. whole wheat flour
½ c. wheat germ
½ c. dry nonfat milk

1 t. baking powder
½ t. cinnamon
1 c. carrots, grated
½ c. raisins
¼ c. walnuts, chopped
1 t. vanilla extract

Per Serving		
Total Fat	4	gm
Saturated	0.3	gm
Unsaturated	3.7	gm
Cholesterol	0.2	mg
Sodium	11	mg
Carbohydrate	11	gm
Protein	2	gm
Fiber	1	gm
Calories	81	

Preheat oven to 350° F. Beat oil, honey, and egg whites together. Separately, combine flour, wheat germ, dry milk, baking powder, and cinnamon; add to batter. Add carrots, raisins, walnuts, and vanilla. Mix well. Drop by teaspoonfuls on two non-stick cookie sheets. Bake for 12 to 15 min.
Prep. time: 40 min. A serving is 1 cookie. *Makes 36 cookies.*

Whitaker Wellness Institute Shopping Guide

Finding fresh, whole, healthy foods or unique condiments can be a bit of a task, but there's an easy way around searching for raw butter or good pastas: catalogues and specialty merchants.

The merchants listed here are reliable and their products are safe and healthy. They use the best ingredients in their foods and beverages, and we trust them. You should too. Not one of them paid to be included in this cookbook. Their names and numbers are here because we wanted to make it easy for you to find the ingredients you need for healthy cooking.

If you can't find something on the shelves of your store, write or call one of these stores. They'll have what you need to cook the way you want.

Cereals, Breads, and Grains

Arrowhead Mills, Inc.
Box 2059
Hereford, TX   79045
806-364-0730
(Rice, grains, cereals, oat bran, pancake mix, cake mix, corn mix, etc.)

Bread Alone
Route 28
Boiceville, NY   12412
800-769-3328
(Fresh baked bread)

Cedarlane Foods Co.
1864 E. 22nd Street
Los Angeles, CA   90058
213-745-4255
(Tanour Bread)

DeBoles Nutritional Foods, Inc.
P.O. Box 2059
Hereford, TX   79045
806-364-0730
(Whole cereals and breads, wheat-free foods)

Garden of Eatin'
5300 Santa Monica Boulevard
Los Angeles, CA   90029
800-333-5244
(Cortillas Corn Tortillas)

Imagine Foods, Inc.
350 Cambridge Avenue
Suite 350
Palo Alto, CA   94306
800-333-6339/415-327-1444
(Rice Dream)

Kashi Co.
P.O. Box 8557
La Jolla, CA   92038-8557
619-274-8870
(Regular & puffed cereals)

Oasis Breads
440 Venture Street
Escondido, CA   92029
619-747-7390

Shiloh Farms
P.O. Box 97
Sulphur Springs, AR   72768
501-298-3297
(Grains & flours)

Good Oils

Healthy Directions, Inc.
P.O. Box 6000
Kearneysville, WV   25430
800-722-8008 ext. 200
(Flax oil)

Spectrum Naturals
133 Copeland Drive
Petaluma, CA   94952
707-778-8900
(Flax oil)

Sauces and Soups

Estee Corporation
169 Lackawanna Avenue
Parsippany, NJ   07054
800-524-1734
(Featherweight Chicken
Bouillon)

Health Valley Foods
16100 Foothill Boulevard
Irwindale, CA   91706
800-742-8238
(Low-salt chili)

Mayacamas Fine Foods, Inc.
P.O. Box 9002
Sonoma, CA   95476
800-826-9621
(Mayacamas Sauces)

Ventre Packing Co., Inc.
6050 Courtstreet Road
Syracuse, NY   13206
315-463-2384
(Pure & Simple Salsa, Enrico's
Salsa & Spaghetti Sauce)

Spices and Condiments

Allied Old English, Inc.
100 Markley Street
Port Reading, NJ   07064
908-636-2060
(Sorrell Ridge Jams & Jellies)

Bernard Jensen Products
P.O. Box 8
Solano Beach, CA   92075
800-755-4027
(Vegetable Broth Seasoning and
other seasonings)

Cumberland Packing Corp.
2 Cumberland Street
Brooklyn, NY   11205
718-858-4200
(Butter Buds, no salt)

Knudsen & Sons
Smucker Quality Beverages
P.O. Box 369
Chico, CA   95927
916-891-1517
(Natural fruit juice and syrups;
ask for local distributor)

Marukan USA (Inc.)
7755 East Monroe
Paramount, CA   90723
213-636-8456
(Rice Vinegar)

Miscellaneous

Body Ecology
2403 4th Avenue
Greeley, CO 80631
800-4-STEVIA
(concentrated natural sweetener)

Buckeyed Beans and Herbs
P.O. Box 28201
Spokane, WA   99228
800-227-1686
(Dried soups, beans, pastas, bread)

Country Life Natural Foods
  Oakhaven
P.O. Box 489
Pullman, MI   49450
616-236-5011
(Beans, nuts, fruits, grains,
pastas, vegetables)

Deer Valley Farm
P.O. Box 173
Guilford, NY   13780
607-764-8556
(Fruits, grains, baked goods,
pastas)

Frontier Cooperative Herbs
P.O. Box 299
Norway, IA   52318
800-786-1388
(Organic herbs and spices)

Garden Spot Distributors
438 White Oak Road
New Holland, PA   17557
800-829-5100
(Baked goods, cereals, grains,
flours, beans, herbs)

Health Valley Foods
16100 Foothill Boulevard
Irwindale, CA   91706
800-742-8238
(Variety of foods)

Healthy Harvest Fruit and
Vegetable Rinse
P.O. Box 861
Madison, CT   06443
203-245-2033

Jaffe Bros.
P.O. Box 636
Valley Center, CA   92082
619-749-1133
(Dried fruits, pastas, grains)

Mountain Ark Trading Co.
P.O. Box 3170
Fayetteville, AR   72702
800-643-8909
(Macrobiotic foods, vegetables)

Pritikin Longevity Center
1910 Ocean Front Walk
Santa Monica, CA   90405
310-450-5433
(Full line of foods)

Walnut Acres Natural Foods
Walnut Acres Road
Penns Creek, PA   17862
800-433-3998
(Poultry, canned soups &
vegetables, grains, seeds, flours,
pastas, dried fruits)

Recipe Index